PUS

Established in 2013 by Joe Eng...
shoestring budget, the facts stack up. PUSH
underground phenomenon. Sold on the street at
football, gigs and any other selling opportunity that
comes his way, this is cutting edge counterculture
literature. In two years, Joe has single-handedly
sold over 4000 copies from out of his selling bag
and through the post. PUSH is a driving force of
subculture and creative identity. Celebrated artists
and writers such as Jah Wobble, Roddy Doyle,
David Peace and John King, have included
themselves among the underground writers and
poets ignored by the mainstream. This is the second
PUSH anthology published by East London Press.

PUSH 2

Edited by Joe England

East London Press

First published in 2015
by East London Press

Introduction © Joe England

Individual work © The Contributors

Cover design by Kosmo Vinyl

Sold on the Street Literature
www.pushmagazine.co.uk

A CIP record for this book is available
from the British Library

ISBN 978-0-9931123-0-0

Printed and bound in the UK
by TJ International
Padstow, PL28 8RW

For Frederick and Flora,

young and gifted,

East London born and bred

The Second PUSH

When I was growing up, I never had any interest in reading or writing let alone editing. My English teacher once screamed at a class one year my junior, who had no doubt got as bored with her lessons as I once did - *Do you all want to end up in a perfume factory like Joe England?*

Harsh words. Because those years in that perfume factory still hold many happy memories to this day. Everywhere back then in any area in the land was territorial, defined by the cult you belonged to, leaned towards; football, punk, 2-tone, reggae, rockers, soul, disco. But that factory drew in young and old from far and beyond, who faced each other every day on the production lines – there were thirteen of them – and you couldn't hide from anyone. So we all talked, suffered Capital Radio, told stories of our lives (most were honest but some tall tales blagged their way in) all to kill time as we waited for the glory moment of clocking out.

But most importantly, day in day out, we connected.

In that perfume factory real friendships were born.

Many have lasted to this day.

But as for school and building the right path for a golden future? I hated it with a passion and, academically, the experience taught me nothing. The main loves from day one were football and music. I wanted to make a living doing either, preferably both. But you need to be very good and lucky to make it.

My football career reads like this: at seven years old I trained with Chelmsford City FC at New Writtle Street stadium – as a guest along with the rest of our small West Ham United kitted gathering – on the morning of a rare appearance for the club in an important round of the FA Cup. One of their players passed me the ball. I stood on it and fell over.

Fast-forward.

I scored two goals in sixty seconds at Arsenal's famous Highbury stadium in a six-a-side tournament. I creamed the moment, but no-one cared. We were already 5-0 up and got knocked out next game. So that's it, what I achieved of note in football. Music delivered slightly more success. I taught myself the bass guitar and played many gigs in many bands, but other than a one year deal with the now defunct Rhythm King Records at the height of Britpop, I was always going to have to keep the day job. However, it was during a visit to Paris to play a gig in the very same band about to be dropped by Rhythm King Records that the word PUSH was to be introduced to me, taking on a dark twist of sorts. Well, not one PUSH, but two.

Rewind.

I suppose there was only one book I read and made an impression on me when I was a small boy. *Flame* by John Pidgeon and published by Panther Books.

And not just because it had swearing in it.

I loved Slade and the film of the book, *Slade in Flame* – the album is brilliant too – but this was my first exposure to a work of fiction that had appeal, depicting the true sleazy cutthroat world of the music industry, and only bettered by John Niven's 2009 masterpiece, *Kill Your Friends*.

In-between reading these two books, I inextricably found an urge to write. I was in another band at the time, and one member of that band ridiculed me for getting above my station. Like, what was I thinking, me trying to write? I reckon he must have been related to my old English teacher.

But I did want to write and I tried to find both a voice and style of narrative. I failed but kept going. I was also struggling to read anything that held my attention. Then one afternoon when casing the bookshelves of WH Smith, I came across an interesting cover. *Untitled Number Two* by Richard Lindner was the kinky artwork. On the back was a suntanned open-legged man with swagger in his eyes and a cucumber down his swim shorts. I opened the book and read: *Joe Orton was born in Leicester in 1933 and battered to death in London in 1967*. That one sentence had me counting out my change, buying the book and reading all his plays within a fortnight. What really attracted me about Orton was the fact that he had no academic background, he was working class and proud and when he got his chance, he pissed on the establishment from a great height. At the same time I realised I could read plays quickly. So I got other Methuen Complete editions; notably Harold Pinter, Brendan Behan. But I didn't become hooked on reading prose until I discovered Kevin Williamson's Rebel Inc Classics. From nowhere I was reading the greatest fiction of the last century. And all published by Kevin. *Ask the Dust* and *The Road to Los Angeles* by John Fante, *Young Adam* by Alexander Trocchi, *Hunger* by Knut Hamsun, *Not Fade Away* by Jim Dodge, *Ringolevio* by Emmett Grogan, the list goes on. All 60 titles were the best thing a person with a new hunger to read could ever dream of. And I had even started to write regularly too.

But not fiction.

West Ham United FC, in the 1980s, always had a healthy wealth of fanzines populating the streets and pubs on match days in London E13. Not all were great, but even the lesser ones had their moments. But I loved them all. *Fortune's Always Hiding, On A Mission From God, On The Terraces, Over Land & Sea, The Water In Majorca*, again the list goes on. The writing was street smart, funny, biting, informative, but always from genuine contributors not wanting their name in lights, just happy to be a part of the culture, the gang; what watching football from a terrace was all about. I began sending my own writing in and was thrilled when I first got published. I must have had something about me, because I ended up with a regular column in one fanzine for nearly four seasons, albeit under another name – I am that shifty.

Fast-forward.

I wrote a few novels too which I never really took anywhere. As I said recently in the *Blackheath Books Counter Cultural Review*, I am not good at dealing with rejection; from girls, publishers, disco dancing competition panelists. So I wrote for myself and a close circle of mates. But through social networking, I began to connect with many writers and poets, who were not only very good, but also had no opportunity to get published other than setting up their own websites/being published on other websites. No-one indulges in reading anything for a sustained period of commitment from a laptop. It is all about what you hold in your hands, that special interaction between author and reader that can only truly be achieved by the printed word.

One night in conversation with East London poet Joseph Ridgwell, I said to him how it was a shame that there wasn't a London based literary fanzine about these days as we both might have had a chance of being published in it.

I said to him: 'Do you know what? I might start one.'

His response: 'Do it then.'

I opened submissions that night and three weeks later I sold the first issue of PUSH on the streets of East London at West Ham United v West Bromwich Albion. I took it to football because it was familiar territory. I knew the streets, the pubs, who to approach. And it sold well, better than I was expecting, as did the next and the next. I appeared to have both the gift of the gab and much luck. What I soon appreciated was this: the writing in PUSH was exciting my readers as much as it had excited me and my contributors. I got many emails saying how the mag was read cover to cover on the way home from the game, while also expressing how the craving to read was always there but the content sought wasn't on any bookshelves, it was clearly to be found in PUSH. I got thanked every time for doing this too.

I was on a winner and each month a new issue came out and was sold out at the next home game. The contributors ensured my inbox was always full and that there was no loss of momentum. All was good. Then came the following season.

West Ham had Stoke City at home and I struggled to sell what was called, 'PUSH 6: The Football Special'. I sold more on the tube to Stoke fans before the game than to any West Ham outside the ground.

On that day, every punter was dressed in just shorts and t-shirts. No jackets or bags to pocket the mag. No-one was interested. I was just another irritant on the street interrupting folk on the way to pub/club/ground. The copies in my selling bag eventually went, but for a while afterwards, I thought that I had definitely taken PUSH as far as it would go. I had lost confidence; my energy levels were drained on that sunny August day.

So after the Stoke game, I seriously thought about jacking it all in and just when I was about to make contact with all the regular contributors, thank them for their great work and support, but explain how it was definitely time to down tools, I got an email from Ian Cusack, a regular since issue 2. David Peace had been promoting his latest work – *Red Or Dead* – and Ian had managed to have a chat with him in Durham and had also passed on a handful of early issues. The feedback from David Peace was exciting and even better, he then asked Ian if PUSH would be interested in doing an interview.

And so began the interviews.

After David Peace, Ian arranged an interview with Roddy Doyle; Joseph Ridgwell interviewed Jenni Fagan and Tony O'Neill and another PUSH regular Allan Wilson interviewed Kevin Williamson, while I went on to interview four important Londoners: Jah Wobble, Grant Fleming, Kosmo Vinyl and John King; the latter two interviews are featured in this book alongside my interview with Raymond Gorman, the former songwriter/guitarist of That Petrol Emotion.

What impressed me was how enthusiastic these great people were to be involved in something so small. They knew this was underground, self-distributed, no glamour, very little if any return, yet they were all happy to be involved and some remain so. It's been a common theme from day one. From those interviewed to all of the contributors and readers. Everyone always – excuse the pun – pushing in the same direction. This journey has been all about momentum and it is a collective momentum. And its drive has always been positive.

Rewind.

So what happened when I was in that band and playing in Paris was this…I was pushed off of a first floor balcony by our drummer. Before all that nonsense happened, I can truly say I liked him. Thought we were mates. But in bands, just like in all human relationships that get tested, minds and emotions can get messed up fast when coming down the other side of the mountain. Helter bleeding Skelter. But I still to this day have no appreciation as to why he pushed me, not once, but twice, as I sat perched on a balcony rail. Why I was on that rail, trying to distance myself from another member of the band, is another story altogether. But all roads connect. If this other band member had pushed me, well, I would have got it. But he was twice my size and even in his most drunken bullying ways, I know he still knew where the line/balcony was drawn. He would have been into a brawl – as we had recently and hence why I needed my own space, chose the balcony as a place of distance – but he was never an attempted murderer. Unlike our most unlikely candidate, Mr Drum. Without warning, Mr Drum arrived from behind the curtain and out onto the balcony and pushed me, unsuccessfully; I managed to grab hold of the rail and pull myself upright. Then our eyes locked tight in a five second freeze frame. Only me and him were in that moment. Was it a joke that backfired? Not sure about that. Because just like the twin towers moment, where the second plane removed all confusion, his madness surfaced and became a truth when he lunged again and over I went.

The cliché says that your life flashes before your eyes when you are about to exit. That is all bollocks. But you do have time, even in a few seconds, to have a think about a few immediate things. I survived, obviously, and even avoided the wheelchair; which I thought was a given as I lay there staring up at the sky. He told the whole world that as I was drunk I had lost my balance and fell, how he had tried to catch me. Nice touch that. For sure, I had been drinking, we had all been drinking, and it was the drink that saved me, allowed me to impact the ground like a rag doll rather than clenched up in panic.

I guess I might sound like I'm bringing this all up as some sort of an opportunist revenge mission. What with the rising success of my literary fanzine. But with this being the second book of PUSH and what with him pushing me twice, well, what I am supposed to do, other than embrace the black magic?

Fast-forward.

When East London Press first approached me and suggested they wanted to publish an anthology – the best of the first 10 issues – I had no idea they would be knocking on my door again so soon. This isn't the best of the next 10 issues because as I write, issue 17 – with an interview with Thurston Moore – has just come back from my printer and all round good man Jim Dalton.

But since those early issues, PUSH has grown in size, look and quality. That is why I understood the drive of East London Press to put out a second book so soon after the first.

As was put to me by the publisher and immediately grabbed my attention:

'What literary magazine has ever put out two anthologies within a year let alone what you're doing?'

I gave them the same silent approval to a question as to when they first approached me with this:

'Who has ever got football fans to read poetry before?'

This book is a clear advance on the first. You always have to advance and I am known to make band analogies when discussing how I edit PUSH, the importance of the running order just like live set and album track lists. That's because you have to get the running order right. If side one of The Jam's *All Mod Cons* had opened with 'It's Too Bad', 'Fly' and 'David Watts' instead of 'All Mod Cons', 'To Be Someone' and 'Mr Clean', it might never have made the impact it immediately created at the time. After the music press criticism of their previous album, they might have got shot down while trying to take off. The running order is crucial.

I loved The Jam and I am more than happy to put myself in the firing line here for stating the following: the previous East London Press book, PUSH – best of the first 10 issues, had a very raw but honest intent. Like The Jam's *In The City* debut album. PUSH 2 could have easily been *This Is The Modern World*.

But it isn't.

In my opinion, PUSH 2 has leapfrogged that second album and landed smartly on a lily pad called *All Mod Cons*.

PUSH has, in such a short space of time, grown up. The smartest kid on the underground playground. Not some bully stealing your money, just me selling you the mag to keep for life, while taking your £2 to invest in the next issue. Richard Branson I ain't.

This is a brilliant collection of counterculture fiction, poetry, artwork and photography. I believe in this book because it is honest and all the writing you are about to read comes from genuine people who are driven to write, not glory seekers wanting to be 'a writer.'

The same can be said for the artwork by Jose Arroyo and photography by Paul Talling.

Having now had the pleasure of meeting most within these pages, I know this as true.

When John King, author of such great works as *The Football Factory*, *Human Punk*, *White Trash* and *The Prison House*, wrote an introduction to the first PUSH book – what many have said is a rallying call-to-arms manifesto against the publishing mainstream – I felt like we had all arrived. Because in a small but glorious way, we had. And so, thanks to East London Press, here we all are again.

Joe England
July 2015

PUSH 2

IN ORDER OF APPEARANCE:

P.A. LEVY – The 'We' Lies

MICHAEL KEENAGHAN – Turbulence

JOSEPH RIDGWELL – Ode To The Lost Boozers of East London

DICKSON TELFER – Nose Art

TIM WELLS – Mary Millington Visits Leyton Orient FC

SIMON DENT – Gunships

JAMIE HALL – Nuisance

IAN CUSACK – Home Game

JARED A. CARNIE – Three Goals Last Season/Takeaway

ANNELIESE MCMILLAN GREGG – Young

STEVE FINBOW – Down Among The Dead

JOHN KING Interview

JOHN KING – The Terror Fantastic

FORD DAGENHAM – They Launched

JIM GIBSON – Old Town

NOT JUST ABOUT THE WRITING:

JOSE ARROYO
pages 21, 55, 93, 121, 197
@paisalogist

JANETTE BECKMAN
page 187
janettebeckman.com
@janettebeckman

PAUL TALLING
pages 137, 155, 178, 217
derelictlondon.com
@derelictlondon

P.A. LEVY

The 'We' Lies

After reading Simone Weil
you put on a pair of sunglasses
and stated emphatically
that every sentence
beginning with 'we' is a lie.

We are good together.

I asked about the sunglasses;
it was January. You explained
with a Gallic shrug she was French
then started reading aloud
long passages, I've no idea
what about 'cos the West Ham
game was on the radio,
the Upton Park faithful
were chanting:
'We are staying up.
We are staying up.'
That doesn't look likely;
lost again.

We were meant for each other.

I opened a bottle of beer
hoping to drown defeat:
trust me to support such
a shit team. You poured yourself
a glass of Burgundy, still feeling French
you tell me: 'we have our liberty.'
To be honest, at this precise moment,
I would rather have three points.
Then, lighting a Gitanes, and surrounding

yourself in plumes of smoke for support
you chant with a smile: 'we have
everything we ever dreamed of.'
Sorry, but I can't see my Triumph Bonny
parked outside. No platinum discs
from my hit records, no cup winners' medals
even though I always score the winning goal.
You see, she could actually be right,
this Simone Weil, 'cos this 'we'
doesn't seem to be working for me.

We would always be true.

With full continental temperament
you allow your arms an acid house
dance; big box, little box,
throw your arms into explaining
about the meaning of the box,
the purpose of its existence.
You exhale Paris itching
to discuss café philosophies
or overturn Renaults
and burn them in the fireplace
waving placards saying:
'we don't talk anymore'.
Sacre Bleu! Merde!
I was telling you we had strikers
that couldn't hit a shot on target
from inside the six yard box,
that our midfield had gone missing,
keeper tends to flap on crosses.
Talking isn't the problem.

We loved each other, once.

Not every sentence
beginning with 'we' is a lie.

MICHAEL KEENAGHAN
Turbulence

I haven't been out for a drink in weeks, have hardly left the flat. But it's Friday night, so I think fuck it, and head out; I've been spending too much time alone with my thoughts and it isn't me, I need to get out there and start living again or I'll end up losing it.

I step out on to the street. I scan left and right assessing threats, exit points, before making my move. I've been home for six months – a civvy now – but old habits die hard. In the Black Horse, I lean by the bar. The blokes all next to me have fallen silent, and I'm waiting an age before the barman finally shifts his arse.

'Look Sean, you know you're barred.'

'Come on Tone, that was weeks ago.'

He shakes his head, says the governor would sack him. So I move on. I stop for a fag outside the Nelson, my heart hammering now. I stand sucking in the smoke trying to relax. Okay, take two. I walk in, order a pint and get served no problem. I spot a few faces I know, but approaching them doesn't seem right somehow. At a nearby table sit Chris and Bill, two mates, but no matter how hard I stare they're doing everything they can to avoid my eye. Then Dave Jennings walks out of the gents clocking me straight away.

'Sean mate,' he says, coming over.

He used to go out with my sister, until he got himself ten months for assaulting a copper. We get chatting, then I notice Chris and Bill putting their coats on.

'Tell me,' I ask, nodding to the departing couple. 'Do I fucking smell or something?'

'Relax,' Dave laughs. 'Chill out. The night is young and you're itching for trouble already. Live and let live mate. Peace and love, it's a good philosophy. Until club kick out time at least.'

He asks if I've heard about Giggsy, big bloke from school, thought he was hard. I tell him I remember him well and if I saw him nowadays I'd kick him straight in the bollocks.

'No need. He blew his fucking head off with a shotgun. Moved to Welwyn, nice house, couple of kids. Then he comes home one night and his wife's in the buff and there's some bloke running out the back door. That's the reason going round anyway. Probably a load of crap, but you never know though. Can you imagine it? Blood and gore all over the gaff and one of his kids walks in and sees him there. What a cunt.'

I flash back to Afghanistan. The sun high, the birds singing in the trees. But entering the compound it was dusky and teeming with flies. There was the smell of death. Then we saw them. In one corner lay a woman and her two children, riddled head to toe in bullets. In the other lay a man, tortured, mutilated, blood all over the walls. They'd been killed by the Taliban for co-operation with the enemy, their bodies left to rot. But I don't mention this, nodding, fast-forwarding, asking if Dave wants a drink.

'No, I've got to run. Tell you what though, what are you doing tonight? I'm off to meet my bird but we'll be down the Coliseum later. She'll have a few mates there as well,' he winks. 'Come down, elevenish.'

I tell him thanks, and I mean it. After he heads off I lean by the bar and have a think. My last time at the Colly hadn't gone well. Outside I was shouting off and all hell broke loose. Then walking home I bricked an estate agents window, and how I got away with it I don't know. But I can do this. I can go clubbing and have a laugh and leave it at that just like anyone else. It's just a matter of discipline. Keeping a lid on things. Not letting it all get to me. But every day is still so hard. The feelings bubbling up, threatening havoc. Returning home after Helmand was a mindfuck. Nobody gave a shit.

War? What war? Oh that – a load of bollocks. Everything back in England suddenly seemed shallow and meaningless. Everyone reading their papers, staring into their screens, obsessed with trivial shit.

These days, unless I was drinking I could hardly talk to people. The phone rang, people knocked but I wouldn't answer. Pulling my curtains, hiding away, burying my head in my hands, seeing myself back on that hill overlooking the poppy fields. The Taliban had engaged us from below and we were hunched over our sandbags, the lads next to me blasting off machine-gun fire and managing to pin the fuckers down behind a compound wall.

Through his binoculars, the corporal spotted a lookout in a field to the far right, and I positioned my long-range rifle, aligned him in the crosshairs. He was almost certain he saw him on a phone, most likely directing the cunts. Do him, he said. But I hesitated. To me he looked like an innocent farmer standing by his shovel; one of the people we were supposed to be liberating. But he kept on. Do it Sean, slot the cunt, we can't take any chances. Just then there was a burst of incoming fire, so fuck it, I pressed the trigger and he dropped.

The lads cheered. Welcome to the club, Sean. My first kill. But I kept looking through the sight, the man flat on his back, a heavy-calibre bullet that would have torn his insides out. I watched as two young men, his sons, ran to him, their arms flailing with an anguish I couldn't hear. Then we were radioed to halt fire. The Americans were flying in to finish things off. We cheered as the B-1 bomber roared closer, dropping its load clean on the Tallies heads, the compound hiding them reduced to rubble and dust.

But my kill didn't feel right. And sure enough, whispers later came through that the farmer was most likely not involved. Back at base the corporal could sense I wasn't feeling my best.

'Listen Sean, you did the right thing. That bloke was up to something, believe me. Half the intel coming through is a load of shit, take my word for it.'

But he hadn't killed a possibly-innocent unarmed man, I had. And was I supposed to feel proud of that?

'The way to think of it is this,' he continued. 'With each kill we save lives.'

But he was wrong. By slotting that old man I'd probably created a dozen new fighters who wouldn't stop until we were dead.

I snap back to the here and now. A man walks through the door. Scotch Pete. Older bloke. I nod and he nods back. He gets a drink and takes a seat on his own. Once when he'd had a skinful he told me his brother was a Para in the Falklands. Mount Longdon. Hand to hand combat, fixed bayonets, charging through the mud. With a tear in his eye he told me his brother had fought and died like a man, and I agreed with him. I still do.

I knock back a double vodka to cheer myself up. Then I head out, the cool night air welcoming. I walk the mile or so towards the town centre feeling positive now, life so much easier with a gut full of alcohol. Things pick up as I head towards the action, big groups of girls all dolled up in heels, short skirts, enough to make your mouth water. I'm crossing a road, eyes locked on the fittest redhead I've ever seen, when next to me there's a screech of brakes and suddenly I'm staring into headlights.

'Watch where you're fucking going man,' the driver shouts leaning out.

I step back. An Audi full of Asian blokes. Pakistani because I see the flag hanging off the mirror. As the car cruises by, the guy in the passenger seat looks me up and down, muttering something, and I hold his glare, willing him to say something louder, wondering if I've survived Helmand all for a four-onto-one kicking on my own doorstep. But the car moves on. I carry on walking. I pass the Great War memorial almost obscured by bushes, pass

28

the boarded-up cinema, then turn onto the High Street, the pubs loud and bustling. I queue for a KFC and stop to eat it on a bench. Watching the revellers go by, not a care in the world, I see myself a few years younger, remembering how different life was back then. How much easier. But the army offered so much more. And the camaraderie was something I could never experience anywhere else. How many people back here would risk death or a maiming for their mates? Not many. But we were looking out for each other every day non-stop. And if I could have died that day to save Matt Garvey I'd have done that, but he died and I lived.

Matt was my best mate in the team. We were born in the same month, came from nearby towns and people even said we looked similar. Before leaving for the tour he'd married his girlfriend, *in case he never came back.*

Of course you'll be back you prick, I told him at the reception.

We all fucking will.

Six weeks before the end of the tour, we were on patrol near the edge of a cornfield. I was thinking how parts of the Green Zone looked just like England – hedgerows, streams, open fields – when the Taliban took us by surprise, gunfire bursting out from the head-high crops. We dived for cover and the firefight was fierce. Bullets came flying in from a second position, then a third, and if backup didn't hurry we'd soon be surrounded. Matt ran for a better firing line, blasting his gun as he went, and I followed ten metres behind him. He took a Taliban cunt clean down, raking him with bullets, before the blast of a rocket-propelled grenade blew us both off our feet. I lay there in the dust and smoke thinking I was dead.

Then I could move my legs, my arms, and then I was up and running on my feet. But when the dust cleared there was no sign of Matt. The lads gave cover as me and the medic searched for him. We found him twisted and bloody by a bush. His eyes were open, he was still alive.

You'll be alright, I told him, you'll be alright, bullets kicking up dust all around us as we dragged him from the firing line, his face in a grimace of pain until the morphine kicked in.

Finally, base began firing powerful Javelin missiles and mortars, and the Taliban melted back into the fields. Matt was in a bad way, needed hospital attention fast, but helicopters were in short supply and we were waiting an age. Bastards! I shouted, blasting off rounds into the fields. The Chinook finally came down to fly him to Bastion, but by now things weren't looking good. The atmosphere back at base that night was bleak. I lay in a corner on my own, hoping and praying he'd be okay. Then the news came through that everything below the waist had to be amputated. Then two days later he died.

Losing a mate wasn't easy. Not a day goes by without wishing I could have done something. Replaying the scene in my dreams. The explosion, the search, the pain on Matt's face. Then seeing myself in a suicide vest getting close to the cunts in Whitehall. The cunts who really killed him.

I throw my wrappers in the bin and check my phone. Believe it or not, it's time I went clubbing. I stop by an off-licence for two cans of Tennents Super and by the time I've downed them I'm feeling about right. I get past the doormen no problem, walking in, the crowds heaving, music banging. I spot Dave and his female crowd straight away.

'Meet Sean, a good mate of mine,' he says, his arm around me. 'And a good soldier too. He was out fighting the ragheads wasn't he. A fucking war hero if you ask me.'

I'm a bit embarrassed, but Dave is Dave, means no harm, and next thing the girls are flocking around me.

'You owe me a drink for that,' he laughs in my ear and then fifteen minutes later I'm paired off with one of them, a brunette called Claire who had her eye on me from the beginning. She's asking me again what it was like out there, and again I'm deflecting saying the worst thing was the lack of beautiful women – a bit like you. And it's corny but it works, because then she's leaning in and we're kissing, and all I want to do now is bring her home and spend the whole night with her, but instead we're drinking and dancing and getting to know one another and it's all good.

Heading to the bogs I pass Dave who says I bet you're glad you came Sean, and inside I see Chris from the pub earlier. And again he totally blanks me.

'Come on Chris, what have I done?'

He stops.

'Are you serious?'

I tell him I know we had a little row a few weeks back, but it was all just drink, means nothing.

'Really? Last time I saw you, you had your hands around my neck and were calling my mother a cunt. You can't remember that, no? Four blokes had to pull you off.'

'Jesus, Chris, I'm sorry.'

'Apology not accepted. You need help – help in the fucking head and everyone knows it. You can't come back here acting like a maniac, it's not on. Seek help or don't fucking talk to me.'

He walks away. The toilet is empty now. I can't believe I said that – to Chris, a mate. I kick one of the cubicle doors so hard it comes off a hinge. Then I stare at myself in the mirror. I look insane and the scar across my cheekbone is redder than ever. I got that scar standing fifty metres from where four Afghan soldiers stood on an IED, and I'm back on that sun-baked road as clear as day. The Afghan boys liked their weed and opium and as soldiers were pretty useless, but still, they were attached to our team. Now three of them were badly maimed, one completely blown apart. The survivors went into battle shock, yelling and screaming, the medic struggling, and the trees along the road looked hung with tinsel, which I soon realised was glistening strips of flesh, and then we had to search the fields for body parts, an arm here, a bit of a leg there, a severed head face up in a ditch. And things like that can fucking change you.

'Oh there you are,' Dave says, walking in. 'Your bird is looking for you. Thinks you've fucked off.'

He nods me into a cubicle for a quick snort – which is maybe just what I need. Then we're walking across the club and I'm in the corner with Claire and we're snogging away, really going for it now, and she's saying we can go back to hers afterwards if I like, and before I know it it's the last tune of the night then the club is clearing onto the street.

Dave and his bird are queuing by the burger stand and we say goodbye, walking arm in arm along the High Street, Claire carrying her heels as we sway and laugh, stopping in shop doorways to kiss. We pass a bakery where she says she works and I tell her when I pop in I'll be expecting free sausage rolls.

Then I notice a change in her and she says:

'Quick, let's go.'

I look around and spot a group of blokes looking over, a big bastard at the front giving me eyes.

'Do you know that prick?' I ask her.

'He's my ex. He's trouble. He still thinks we're going out. Let's just move.'

She's pulling on my arm. But running away isn't how I do things.

'You got a problem mate?' I call over.

And he's walking towards me.

'Come on then you wanker,' he says, pushing me and it kicks off, the bastard throwing his full weight onto me, but I'm straight back at him kicking and punching.

But then his mates join in, and suddenly it looks like I'm about to get a pasting. The kicks and blows come raining in from all angles, but still I'm on my feet, until the big cunt roars and grabs me, wanting a piece of me all to himself.

Then like a train has hit him he's thrown to the side, Dave Jennings on the scene with a flying kick that fells the bastard.

It's two-onto-four now and we're turning the tables, kicking arse, bodies flying all over the shop. Until a siren ebbs to a halt and the police come charging.

'Don't arrest him, please,' Claire says, as they drag me to the van.

'Don't get involved, darling.'

I see Dave giving his best, two of them struggling with him, his girlfriend making a scene, and notice the fat cunt on the ground face-down, one cuffing him, the other with his pig-issue boot on his head.

'Right, get the fuck in there,' and I'm thrown in the cage.

But I'm riding high. It was a good ruck. Just what the doctor ordered. Instead of a night of female company, I've got a cell to look forward to. But maybe it was worth it. Or so I tell myself.

As the van pulls away, the adrenaline dissipating now, I can see a bewildered Claire standing there, heels in her hand and tears down her face, her figure getting smaller and smaller.

JOSEPH RIDGWELL

Ode To The Lost Boozers
of East London

The boozer or public house
was the lifeblood of the community
in the old East End
two or three in every street
and one on every corner
a meeting place
and social club where
everything happened

Births, deaths, christenings,
weddings, birthdays, funerals
business was conducted,
goods sold, friendships formed
there were knees ups,
sing-a-longs, love affairs
courtships, gambling,
racing, football, darts,
snooker, billiards, bird-fancying
cards, bare-knuckle contests,
cockfights...
...and now
there's not much left

Just ghosts, phantoms and spectres
abandoned by newcomers with a distaste for alcohol
and strange pale-faced goons wired to electric gadgetry
hastening the disappearance of the boozer,
rub-a-dub and ale houses
forever round those sides
or have they?

For signs of their presence
are all around
in different forms and guises

For The Bombay Grab,
you have the Bow Men's Muslim Association
The Blade Bone – a Noodle King
The Frying Pan – A Curry House
Earl of Derby – Children's Nursery
The Two Brewers – Coffee Internet Shop
The Hare – Clothes Wholesalers
Arabian Arms – Gentlemen's Club
The Dolphin – Residential Usage
Duke of Wellington – Commercial Offices
Black Boy – Fast Food Outlet
Grave Maurice – Bookmakers
and on and on

All gone, and along with them the patrons
the barmaids, landlords and landladies
boozers, tarts, gangsters, hard men
swindlers, villains, and terrors

And no more will there be swifties,
sessions, lock-ins, or friendly halfs

No more sprees, or beanos
or one for the Kermit
no more swaying home
by the light of the moon
down side streets and alleyways
arm in arm
one leg lifted high
with never a worry
what the morning might bring

DICKSON TELFER
Nose Art

'Do these definitely work? I mean, do they genuinely cut out *all* background noise?'

'One hundred per cent,' the salesman says. 'Hence the price. You're welcome to give them a try if you want. I can guarantee you though, the only thing you'll hear is the music. It's quite weird actually. But brilliant.'

'Yeah, I'll try them then,' I say.

He goes behind the counter, opens a drawer and lifts out a yellow pair.

'Have you got an iPod or something with you?'

'Yeah, got one here.'

I unplug my naff earphones and stuff them back into my pocket. The salesman passes me the headphones. I put them on and adjust them so they're comfy. I pick Kate Bush's *Hounds of Love* and press play. The salesman laughs at my expression. He says something, but it's like watching TV on mute.

'I'll take them,' I say.

'I thought you might. What colour would you like?'

'Black's fine, thanks.'

'Any deals on today?'

'Yup, we're doing a special on minute steak,' the butcher says. 'Best price in town.'

'I'll take ten,' I say, 'and one steak and kidney pie.'

When I get home, I turn on the oven and prepare the potatoes and carrots. From now on, there'll be no more stab-and-zap junk. I need nutrition. I need to be strong. Things are going to change.

Things *have* to change.

I sit on a stool and watch the pie cook for a while – and the glisten of the oil on the vegetables as they roast. I put my nose in the air and breathe in the smells, a refreshing change from the stench of hot plastic and monosodium glutamate. I try to shut off all other senses and take big, deep sniffs.

Ten minutes to serving time, I take off my t-shirt, drop to the linoleum and start doing press-ups. After 30, my muscles begin to fail and the bruises on my chest and back hurt like fuck. But I keep going. Exertion and the heat from the oven cause me to sweat profusely. I watch bead after bead drip onto the lino and put all my focus into creating a puddle; anything to take away from the pain. I keep pumping, the air now thick with the scent of steak and kidney pie and roast veg, but I don't quite make it.

When the buzzer sounds, I'm lying face down in a pool of sweat. I carefully prise myself up and mop up the mess with kitchen roll. I look into the oven and manage a smile.

I have a quick wash, put on a clean t-shirt and then serve up the pie.

I sit in my dining room.

Alone.

In silence.

I look at the photographs on the wall. And eat, knife and fork shaking. I suck bits of meat, draining them of gravy, feeling the dead flesh in my mouth. Once I've finished, I drink a pint of water but nearly drop the glass as my muscles burn and twitch.

When I leave the house, I look back at the living room window. It's just a habit, like looking back at my seat when I get up to get off a train. I put up my hood and march off up the road.

When I get there, I put on my gloves and balaclava then unlock the hut. Both of them futilely flail about on the floor like worms, the gaffer tape still tight around their ankles and wrists. The tape around their heads and mouths muffles their screams. Having left only their eyes and noses uncovered, their hair tufts out the top of their heads like the crown of a pineapple. Piss soaks their jeans and the skinny one is shivering. Over the other side, the dogs are going mental in their cages. They've only had each other for company for the last two days.

I open my rucksack and pull out a kitchen knife. Their muffled screams go up a notch. I cut off their jeans, shirts and boxers, nearly gagging on the stale reek, then apply more tape to their ankles, just in case the piss has slackened it a bit. I try not to laugh. The severed jeans poking out from the top of the tape, their tiny cocks retracted in the cold. I look at the fear in their eyes, darting from one to the other, and then glance up at the scarf tied to one of the rafters, disgusted to be looking at colours that usually generate feelings of loyalty and pride.

I open my rucksack, pull out the minute steaks and smear the raw meat across their bruised flesh. I cut through the tape on the mouth of the skinny one.

'You fucking cunt, you'll fucking pay for th…'

I stuff the piece of steak I've just rubbed his crotch with into his mouth and then tape it shut with three tight layers.

'We know where you live, you cunt, you're going to…' the other one says, as I give him the same treatment.

'I know you do,' I say. 'I know you do.'

Once I've tied a steak to each of their throats and crotches, I lock the hut and walk across to the dogs' cages. I look at the poor bastards as they go crazy, jumping up, foam dripping from their mouths, fangs bared like hungry, angry vampires. There are two padlocks on the cage. I unlock the top one and replace it with one of my specials. Once it's secure and the little light has gone red, I repeat the process for the bottom one, the dogs' savage faces only centimetres away.

Bits of foam and saliva hit my balaclava. The little light goes red and I look at the dogs, water filling up in my eyes.

'It's not your fault, pals,' I say.

I go back to the hut and drag them into the centre of the arena one at a time, the fatter one first. I close and lock the gate and pull the controller from my rucksack, along with my iPod and new headphones. I put the headphones on, but not fully, the right pad only covering half my ear.

I turn my back on the arena, start walking and press the button on the controller. It beeps, the light on the plastic facing turning from red to green. I secure the right pad, press play and head home.

I notice purple marks on people's fences, or on the kerbs in front of their houses.

Their dogs are safe now.

They don't know it – nor will they ever – but I'm their hero.

Once I get home I crack open a beer and sit in my living room, in darkness.

The glow from the streetlights illuminates Judy's nose marks on the window. She would always be there, back paws on the armchair, front paws on the windowsill, whether I was leaving or arriving. My loyal friend. Nose art, my mum called it. Like Judy was painting pictures with her nose.

These shapes will never change now.

I look at her final masterpiece and cry my eyes out. Again. Wanting nothing more than this to be a horrible dream and that she'd pad in, wagging her shiny black tail, and I'd feel the love of her soft, pink tongue on my hand.

TIM WELLS

Mary Millington Visits
Leyton Orient FC

If she did actually come
I wasn't there, or at least
don't remember it.
She did tour
most of the arse ends
of England.

Those seventies mags
are full of arseholes,
of both sorts;
but visit she would,
and turn those visits
into seedy stories –
generally the same one.

To be fair,
porn's not relished
for plot devices
and characterisation.
The protagonists
tend to be parodies,
but always recognisable.

And that's the joy
of Mary Millington;
whether at the football,
the chip shop
or on the factory floor,
all seemed possible.
Revealingly bent over a cab,
thrusting out of maxi coat –
that hard-earned 50p
spent on the same old thing.

SIMON DENT
Gunships for Katie Hopkins

you sneer & grin disgust at us like
we are all born from whores
lottery ticket winning cockroaches
escapees from abortion
you want us dead; well we are all now dead
in our fucked up desperation
we paid more than you'll ever earn
to get packed into a floating sardine can
the size Gulliver bought from Lidl
for a handy lunchtime fingered snack
and then we went and capsized and drowned
all before your gunships arrived

JAMIE HALL
Nuisance

I was strolling about the house minding my own
business when the phone rang. I shouldn't really
have answered it but I did. Some lady on other end
began telling me that I was entitled to some money
because of an insurance claim and that I'd maybe
had a car accident. So after I disagreed with her
about 3 times, I finally decided to tell her that I
don't actually live here and that I was robbing the
house. Cos I was. For the first time in history one
of these pests went and hung up before I could.

IAN CUSACK
Home Game

Metallic alarm clang splits open your dream of rocks and the ocean breaking on Malin Head. Force yourself conscious. Sleep already a memory as you sit upright, blinking. Six o'clock. Early enough, but you're a worrier when it comes to connections. No time for idling. Jagged toenails click on purple nylon sheets. Crawl from under the blanket and candlewick and into Saturday. Rearrange the covers so there's no draft on her back and she can lie on. Curse the bed springs' twang. Suppress a cough. Sweep up an armful of clothes from the seat at your side of the bed. Shiver. Bare feet stick to chilled lino. Mid March. Still feels like winter. Clocks go forward in a fortnight. You'd have a holiday on Monday back home. Not here. It's a normal day. Work. And that's why you came, but not why you stayed. You're stood in the doorframe, gripping the handle. Eyes coping with the darkness. A glance over your shoulder. The outline of her back. Hair spread out across the pillow and beyond. That surge of love still overwhelms you. Heart lurches every morning when you say goodbye.

A dozen years now. Almost to the day. Everyone told you she would be trouble. The kid, just out of nappies and no sign of a father. You knew it wasn't like things back home. She was the one. A keeper. She stirs a fraction, mutters in her sleep then dives deep below the surface of consciousness and you close the door behind you. Gently. Cross the landing on tip toe. In the bathroom and a dirty green piss. You sit down to muffle the noise and so as you don't splash the floor. She hates that. On the throne with nothing to read but Wednesday's 'Standard.' Schoolboy error. Like the West Ham defending against Notts County, or so it says. You've been doing your homework. One set of Magpies on Tuesday and today it's the other Magpies, or so you've learned. Forty years of age and your first trip up north. Ridiculous. Shake the head loose of your daydreams. Too early for a shite. Tea and fags will sort that out later. Lather up and rinse round the face and neck, then under the pits and finally your feet. Water turns grey and leaves a trail of scum on the sink side when you let it go. No need to shave. You did that last night, while she watched the telly. Bath and an early night before the big day. Fuck knows how you're dirty this morning. Scalding water straight from the tap and then a warm towel off the radiator. Instant heat amazes you. The best thing ever. Civilisation's greatest luxury. Brush the teeth with that minty stuff she's been buying. Almost stings the mouth off you, but in a good way. Stare out into the shrinking dark as you get dressed. Blank sky. New moon. The vague outline of hundreds of houses. Just like this one. All in a long line. Maybe two or three with their lights on. Early risers. Forgetful drunks. Concerned parents who left the one in the passage burning overnight to calm fretful kids. You don't know. You don't know any of them. Millions of people all over this city using all their money to buy identical brick boxes to help them remain anonymous. Invisible. Ten years you've owned this place and you don't know a soul from your next street.

At home everyone knew each other in your town and the next one and most folk in the one after that. Over here there's a few from work you get on with, great for a pint now and then, but you only truly know her and the young feller. At least you used to know him. Coming up 16. No longer a boy. Flinches when you say rashers instead of bacon or soccer instead of football. Taken to calling you Don as it makes you sound less foreign. That wounding look of contempt he gives you when he catches you talking about your home town. But you'll always be there for him. You promised her that from the start. You're not his dad, but you're the next best thing. You've given him a good home, never raised your fist and you keep trying your best to get on. That's what today is about. You stand ready to knock him awake, but there's a pale beam seeping under his door. 40 watt bedside lamp. Probably fell asleep reading. Penguin modern classics. Camus. Kafka. Sartre. French and German blokes you've never heard of. Translated but. That or listening to the radio. Capital. The only music you can hear before dawn in a city of 7 million people. Fern Kinney at number 1 singing 'Together We are Beautiful.' Awful shite. You leave him a while longer as you head downstairs to fix a bit of breakfast.

One stair creaks. The cracked tread you forgot to replace. You curse but know the sound's not enough to wake her. Or him. Fluorescent strip light on. Harsh and clinical brilliance. On the table, there's a feast. She's done you proud. Rounds of sandwiches. Wrapped in Clingfilm. Cheese. The sliced stuff he likes and some tomatoes in yours as well. Sausage rolls. Hard boiled eggs and a pinch of salt in a twist of brown paper. Penguin biscuits. Oranges. You blink out tears of love and gratitude then put the kettle on. It's the small things. A smoke at the back door while the tea brews. Dew on the washing line and the end of the lawn illuminated by the kitchen light. Clouds of smoke and breath vapour disappear as the blackness above turns to a grey dawn. Three cups. You drain yours, scalding the throat off you, then take the other two upstairs. Tap on his door. A grunt. Set the cup on the floor. Back in your room. Diagonal slice of light across her left arm, as she grips the blankets close. You silently place the tea at her bedside. She knows you're there. Keeps her eyes closed but smiles. Drops the covers. Holds out her arms. Whispers that she loves you and now you don't want to leave. Let him go 300 miles up country for some fucking stupid game and you'll stay with her. In each other's arms. But you promised. So you sit on the chair at her side and stoop over. Hold her close as you can. Nuzzle her hair. Say you love her too. Fish two biscuits out your shirt pocket for the tea. This makes her giggle and stroke the bump on your nose where that cunt in the King Eddie's smashed it with a stool because he blamed you for some fucking bombing you'd never even heard about. But you forgot your anger when you came home. She bathed the blood and the tears away. Placed a hand on your heart to slow your fury and promised you'd never suffer hatred again. You understood. The time had come. You moved. Not far. A few miles north. Put your money into property and not across the bar. Became a family. You'll be grateful for that until you die. No words. Holding her is the only way to say thanks. Then that sadness because you never gave her another kid wells up. And then the young feller explodes out of his room, clatters downstairs like an Alpine rock slide and calls out it's time to go. So you and her exchange a final smile and you start to head. You're leaving and it hurts, but she blows you a kiss when you stop at the door and it has to be enough. You close it behind you. Framing her image. Knowing she'll be back asleep by the time you're at the foot of the stairs.

The front door's open and the lad's sat on the front wall, shovelling a sausage roll down him with the rest of the food in a bag. He waves it at you and you take responsibility. Walk down the empty street, swinging the bag as you go. See the fading redness in the whitening sky over Lloyd Park. Rustle of birds. No traffic drowning them out. Head west down Forest Road towards the tube. Cars and houses asleep. Wave down a milk float. A pint for you and a carton of juice for him. Cold like it's been in the fridge. Shudder as you drink and shrink down into your overcoat. *You're getting old* his look tells you. T-shirt and a Wrangler jacket enough to keep him warm.

That and the scarf. Claret and blue. There's no county wears those colours you told him when he'd picked West Ham as his team 5 years back. It wasn't your game, same as Gaelic and the hurling have never been his, but you tried to understand at least. Pointed out Tottenham's ground across the river and past the reservoir, but he wasn't interested. He was West Ham and he wanted to know who you were for. You thought of Walthamstow Avenue, on the doorstep and a name that made you laugh, but you picked Norwich. Jerseys the same as Donegal. He cried when they lost the League Cup to Villa. Suffered the pain you didn't feel. Another team in claret and blue, but that didn't matter to him. Promised you West Ham would win the FA Cup to make things better. He was right. Alan Taylor. Twice. He shared his joy and it was the best day you'd ever had together. You were his other hero for getting a colour telly in time for the final. All summer he nagged you to take him to a real game. She gave her blessing. Thought it would be good for the both of you. Start of the next season. Late August Bank Holiday. Spurs at home. Won 1-0. Happy times, but you never went again. Loads of reasons. Always an excuse. Working all the time to pay the mortgage, or spending your spare time doing the house up. Him starting big school. Homework and the athletics he had a flair for. Skinny. Sharp knees and shoulders. Elbows. On the track in the summer and the cross country in the winter. Out every weekend running. The odd night game with his mates from school whose dads understood the game. Highbury. White Hart Lane. Even over to QPR, but he was the outsider when the Irons in his soul. Saturday afternoons in the bath, washing the mud from his legs. Radio tuned to LBC for the updates. He'd tell you the score and you'd sympathise or congratulate, going on instinct. Time passed.

Six months and he'll be 16. His future is A levels, university and all that, but still there's the soccer. Now he wants to travel away. Reasoning he can get to see different cities and have a feel for them before applying to study there. You don't know. She tells him when he's of age he can please himself, but until then he wasn't travelling 300 miles up the country on his own. So you'd volunteered. He picked a vague date on the calendar and you'd agreed. A chance to mend what hadn't been broken. Just became frayed with neglect. You both drain your drinks and leave them on the pavement outside the tube. Returns to Kings Cross and a five minute wait. Still early. Platform deserted. No office workers on a Saturday and too early for shoppers. In the smoking carriage. Ghosts of dark blue smoke. He folds his arms. Shuts his eyes. Still scrawny. Downy fuzz on his top lip that's never seen a razor. You yawn. Only 18 hours before you can get back to bed. And her. Last night's 'Standard' on the seat opposite, open at the inside back cover. Lyall promising to put things right, though admitting Newcastle's a tough place to visit. You turn the pages, then close the paper. Fold it up and throw it on the floor. Colours. Allegiances. Geography. Spurs territory gives way to Arsenal territory. Cockerels. Gunners. Hammers. Magpies. Kings Cross. Tea and a paper for you, but he's itching to be on the train, urging you to hurry up though there's half an hour yet. Gulp it down then head for the station. Check again for the envelope in the back pocket of your strides. Flap buttoned on it and your wallet. Tickets. You show him. His face falls. He thought you were going on the special. You try to explain it's a treat. More comfortable. Safer. Guaranteed window seats. He snorts. You shrug. A failure. No blood. No connection. You both see the special's queue start to move. A fringe of coppers dwarfing and masking the shouting West Ham fans. Ushering them onto the train. It's leaving in 5 minutes. Disapproving glances at the lads singing. Like a strict primary school at home time. Hundreds of lads about the young feller's age in jeans and jackets and t-shirts and scarves. He looks at you with pleading. You check the tickets and think fuck it. You're with his tribe. You can go with them.

He's running now and you're doing the fast walk to keep up. Tea and milk and fags working on your guts and bladder. He turns, scarf above his head in triumph, shouts thanks and disappears onto the train. You're almost breathless as you stumble down the platform looking for him. It's a blur of scarves, flags and faces. All shouting. All happy. The doors are closing, so you climb on. Pushing and squeezing your way forwards. Relentlessly apologising. Funny looks. Must be the accent. Or your age. You see him in a carriage with some lads he seems to know. Sixth formers from school. Maybe, but they look a bit rough. Hair's awful short. But he's happy enough. Daft ones sitting in the luggage racks. Legs dangling. Bright red boots. Yellow laces. Loud chat about bands and girls, so you wink and walk on. He appreciates that. Dive into the jacks and drop a load. Clean and empty, you're back out again as Potter's Bar gets left behind and the day is beginning. You find a double seat in with the older fellers up the front. Blokes in caps. Newspapers. Decks of cards. Flasks. Conversation not shouting. Nobody sits next to you, so you take off your coat and roll it up like a pillow. Soon you're back on Ballyhillion strand, staring out at the Inistrahull lighthouse. Face full of salty wind when you were a boy. You wake much later and the young feller's next to you. Asleep. His head leaning into you and a book in his hands. Kafka. *Metamorphosis*. You take it from him and flick through the pages uncomprehendingly. He stirs and smiles as he comes awake. Happy to be in each other's company, you share the sandwiches and talk. He tells you about the game and who to look out for as the train passes the cathedral and castle of Durham. Getting close now. Picking up speed. Picking up noise. Picking up adrenaline. Everyone is blowing bubbles, apart from you, until he encourages you to join in and immediately you're both singing and laughing and the world is a great fucking place as the train slides into the station.

Except it isn't the actual station. It's a siding in some goods yard. The train doors burst open and by the time you're outside, it's clear this shed like a barn is as far as anyone is going for a while. Coppers are everywhere. Directing you all into a holding area. Pushing. Shoving. Battering lads for giving them lip, or even for looking at them funny. Everyone penned in together. A senior copper in a peaked cap up on a raised gangway, shouting through a megaphone. Demanding silence. Obedience assured through indiscriminate blows of the truncheon. Your idea was for a few pints. Maybe a trip to the bookies. That's gone. You're told everyone will be marched from the station to the ground. No exceptions. Anyone breaking ranks, complaining, shouting or otherwise making a nuisance will be arrested. Then kicked to fuck someone adds and you all laugh until a copper lays the young joker out cold with a blow across the small of his back. Three of them drag the kid away. Face bouncing off tarmac and concrete. Unconscious but still blindly accepting a hiding. Aware of your age, your accent and your fear, you place a possessive arm round the young feller's shoulders and talk in whispers as you're marched like criminals or collaborators through the streets.

Cold bright day. Your head's spinning. Tension and tiredness. People you've never met from a place you've never been are calling you all sorts of cunts. Hatred. Same as you felt in the King Eddie, except now you're been taunted for being a Cockney bastard. You look round to try and understand what makes some lad who's never seen you before say those sorts of things, but this copper is pushing you forwards. Keeping everyone's eyes straight ahead. Stopping lads from singing. The regular sound of yelps after blows and kicks and digs. Vans crawling alongside. Ones with the doors open full of coppers. Angry. Moustaches. Blazing eyes. Ones with the doors shut full of young lads. Bleeding. The smell of a brewery masking the smell of young male terror and malevolence and your incomprehension of a game and a country you still don't understand. At the young feller's age you'd crisscross the border for Ulster championship games. Hitching lifts from lorries and tractors. Some towns you went through acted closed on a Sunday and flew Union Jacks, but that's the way it was in the days before rock and roll. You didn't hate what you didn't know. Unlike here. Unlike now.

At the ground, you try to act the peacemaker. Play up the accent talking to the blokes on the gate. Buy a programme with a fiver. Pretend you don't know the price of stuff. Thick Paddy out of his depth. Ask about getting up in the seats. One of the blokes starts pointing you in the direction, until some angry copper tells you to hurry up or he'll lift you, so in you go, head bowed and take your place on the crowded terrace with the young feller, whose eyes betray a level of fear you've never seen in a human before. You know that both sides have picked the wrong lot to hate. It's not the black and white or the claret and blue you should fear, but your ones in the uniforms. Bastards. 'I'm scared,' he tells you 'So am I,' you reply.

Glance at your watch. Two hours in the ground. An hour more in the city and then your escape on the train. 180 minutes to survive. More and more West Ham arrive. Your little bit of concrete is packed out. You get pushed from behind and lose your place on the step. All you can do is push back to get next to the young feller. Other side of the railing thousands of Magpies on the same sort of concrete steps. Swearing. Jeers. Up to your left in the seats it's no better. Home fans shouting terrible things.

Gestures. Hate. Hate. Hate. Contorted faces. Nobody is looking at the pitch. A shower of loose change from some West Ham boys behind you sparks a volley of glass and metal in return. You stand half in front of the young feller. Tell him to keep his eyes on the game and you'll watch out for missiles. He tries a half smile. It doesn't come off. All around you the lads, not even grown, impersonate violent, evil men. Where are their dads to sort this out? Explain it's wrong and that we're all the same. All here for the game surely. Maybe their dads don't care or have given up. Thrown up their hands in despair. Or maybe they're like your young feller with no real father, only you and your best intentions to help him find the way through life. Right now all you can do is form an inadequate shield against torrents of brick fragments and rusty debris, bolts harvested from factory floors that pour down from a sky full of lead. You want to escape. To escort the young feller away from this madness. Race down the hill and onto the train back home.

Then it happens. A petrol bomb. A flaming bottle like you've see on the news from Belfast arcs through the air, describing a neat parabola above their fans, across the fence separating the two sets. You see it. Frozen. Silent. An age as it falls. You think it's going to hit you and instinctively you crouch, pulling the coat across your head as a cloth barrier, but it sails past and shatters in the throng of West Ham behind you, who scatter as fire bursts upwards. The screams of children. A vision of hell. The young feller with his Wrangler on fire alone in the midst of this insanity. Arms aloft like some crazed preacher or dazed stunt man, he stumbles across the emptying terrace in freeze frame as those around him retreat blindly, squealing. You move. Without thinking. A rugby tackle brings his bony knees and extended palms down hard as you both bounce on the concrete steps. Your old coat denies the fire any oxygen and you squeeze him downwards. Your pressure and the woollen vacuum snuff the blaze out. Acrid burnt cloth and hair stink neutralised by competing odours of burgers, beer and sweat as the crowd throngs. People reclaim their vantage points.

He's scorched and screaming, as you remove his charred jacket. But he's alright. He's okay. No burns. No cuts. Crying and disorientated, but there's no injuries, only a pervasive residual fear that you need to control. Hug it out of him. Everything's grand you tell the watchers. You don't mind the blisters on your hands or the cold that the day is challenging you with. Worst of it are the scorch marks on the lining of your old coat. You wrap it round his convulsing shoulders like it's the beach towel you dried him with after you went swimming at Tullagh Bay that August you took her and the young feller over on holiday. That was when you knew what you'd called home could never be home again, because of the way people stared at her and him whenever they talked. The silence in cafes and the whispering as you left again. You have to let it go. The anger. It gains you nothing. A copper leads you and him away, down the back of the terracing, through the guts of the stand and into a First Aid room. The game goes on. The two sets forget you as the shouting and roaring starts up again. A St John's Ambulance bloke looks the two of you over. Puts a bandage on your left hand where it's blistered. Gives you both sugary tea and a chance to sit a while. There's a Newcastle lad flat out on his side. Unconscious. In the recovery position. He's fainted they tell you. Let him sleep you say. 'Sure it won't be the excitement that's done for him,' says the St John's bloke and you realise you don't know the score. You're free to go, so you ask the young feller if he wants to see the rest of the game and he shakes his head, looks at the floor with his hands clasped between his thighs. Still fearful, but he's safe now. A copper leads you to an exit gate.

Ignored, you leave the ground and head away from the noise, into the body of the city where thousands go about their business, but none of them throwing things or calling at you. You find a clothes shop. One of those boutique places, but for men. Young men like him. Pausing outside, you take his scarf and his book for safekeeping. Throw the burnt Wrangler in a bin and buy him a new one. A bigger size. Longer on the arms and at the back as he's growing. Taller than you by half a head. A fine specimen. You're proud. His thanks are genuine and again you're biting back the tears. Claiming it's nothing. And you both realise it's time to go. A walk to the station. Stop for fish and chips to take out. Eating them as you go, you grab some drink for the journey. Commentary on the radio in the beer shop calls the game a disgrace. On and off the pitch. At the station you're in luck. Ten minutes until the train. Earlier by an hour than you'd anticipated. Brisk walk to the platform. Pump your last ten pence's in a call box to tell her...tell her what? Tell her nothing. It was a grand day, but the game was rotten. She confirms the result. 0-0. Just up on the teleprinter. These English games are a waste of time, you tell her. She laughs. And the pips go, so you tell her you love her and seconds later you're on the train.

There's nobody else in the carriage. It's warm and the cloth seats sag affectionately. He settles down with his book and you flick through the programme. Blurred pages full of statistics you've no interest in. So you open a can. Take a slow drink watching the north go by as the sky darkens. Eating up the ground towards your destination. Putting distance between you and the madness and hatred. You've been up twelve hours. There's 300 miles still to go, but you're going home. Together. You settle back, close your eyes and soon you're dreaming of her hair spread out across the pillow and beyond.

JARED A. CARNIE

Three Goals Last Season

One time he saw his dad kick the dog in the stomach.
Another time the dog bit him on the leg.
At school a girl took his pencil case.
He punched her in the eye and got expelled.

At his new school he didn't have the uniform.
The other kids noticed.
He stood in the playground screaming.
He would take on anyone who dared.

Rory dared.

Rory lived with his mum.
One night she was waiting for her husband.
She had a bottle in her hand.
She saw him come out of the pub.
With his arm around that bitch.
She cracked him over the head.

Rory was up when she got home.

She had blood on her hands and a smile on her face.

Most weeks he and Rory fought each other.
While the other kids watched.
They understood each other.

Last year he was in the passenger seat,
when Rory smashed into a lamppost.

It was in the paper.

The headline said:

TEEN DRINK DRIVE DEATHS

At their old school they have a plaque in the corridor.
Saying that a West Ham player used to go there.

They're very proud of that.

Takeaway

He's drunk in the Indian.
Can barely stand.
Can hardly talk.
He's getting aggressive.
He's getting physical.
They won't serve him anymore.

'You fucking Paki,
you take my money for food,
but you won't give me drink.
I'm a paying customer,
and I want two pints
and I want them now.'

He sees three women.
Eating in the corner.

'Excuse me ladies,
pardon the language...'

Because, you know,
with the fairer sex around,
that sort of thing,
really isn't on.

x

57

ANNELIESE MCMILLAN GREGG

Young

Give me cause
to think
that your callowness
is not
a hollow song
so high and sweet
and sounding with the spring
you lick the plumpness of the skin
in lime green grapes
that hang
in jewelled clusters
below your song
of bang and birth

But where were you
when the dewy eyes of dawn
collided with the dusk
and the radiance of youth
was closed over
darkened
by the cataracts of old

Where were you
when the fruits were crushed
and bruised
when perfect
underfoot
to make the wine
that now I drink?

STEVE FINBOW
Down Among The Dead

Gibraltar, March 1988

Voices wake me. Hotel workers on the terrace. Voices amplified by the garden walls. A smeared sound. Nothing discernible. A low hum. I look at my watch – 6:45am. I roll back the covers, rub my forehead, open the curtains, look out the window. A man rakes leaves from the pool. A woman covers four poolside tables with cloths and arranges cutlery that glints and throws quick messages in the morning sun. I turn on the shower, step in. The water tastes metallic, salty. The hotel soap smells of rotten roses and has the consistency of marshmallow. My hair refuses to lather. I rinse, dry myself, clean my teeth, brush my hair. I dress in beige chinos, a pale-blue cotton shirt, brown moccasins. I drape a dark-blue sweater over my shoulders. At the last minute, I decide to wear sunglasses. I wasn't going to bring them, thinking they'd make me look too conspicuous but everyone here wears them.

While I'm dressing, I make a cup of instant coffee. The kettle refuses to boil and the water is cooler than the shower and tastes about the same, the saltiness undercutting the cheap coffee's ripe bitterness. I take my camera case from my holdall. Your man would have a fit if he saw it, but there's no camera. I carry the case because it's handy for holding my book, passport, and wallet. My stomach feels hollow. I don't know whether it's nerves or hunger. I walk down to the breakfast room. I load my plate with ham, cheese, fruit, a bread roll. The coffee is much better than that shite in the room, so I help myself to two cups. On a chair by the door, someone has left a Daily Mirror. I read it while I drink my coffee. The pool looks inviting but I think I'll walk around the town, maybe go to the top of the Rock, have a look at the view, get a glimpse of the apes. I've got a bit of time on my hands. I get a map from reception, head out into the streets.

People are on their way to work. Tourists head to the seafront while waiting for the museums and shops to open. I look at the map, decide to walk through the streets, taking my time to memorise the buildings. Get my bearings. I once spent a week in Florencia, Colombia, in bed with food poisoning, another week twiddling my thumbs in a hotel room in Tripoli, and three weeks in Donostia-San Sebastián eating tapas while talking revolution and mayhem with mad Basque bastards. Here I am on the other side of the country waiting to follow three youngsters with more guts than I've ever had. I am the go-between, the smoother, the oiler, the one with the ready smile, the unsweaty handshake. Want someone to look normal – send Michael. Want someone who won't start a fight in a local bar – send Michael. Never a problem. Dependable. Look like what I pretend to be – a salesman. When the Brits searched me – which they did on a regular basis – they found pamphlets for the wee plastic thingamies I was supposed to sell. Your man had had his brother-in-law print the pamphlets for me – made a change from Chinese take-away menus. Wellington Front, past the cannons overlooking the harbour, down to the Ragged Staff Gates, past John MacKintosh Hall, back through the Grand Parade, into the Alameda Gardens overgrown with jasmines and jessamines, wisteria and wild olives, feral cats slinking through the undergrowth. Over birdsong and the scurrying of the lizards, it came to me that this place was the British Empire in miniature with its cannons, guns, the Iron Duke's memorial, Trafalgar cemetery, Nelson's anchorage. That's what they're doing here. Jesus, don't tell me they actually have a purpose. Your man wouldn't like me thinking that way. It's 10a.m. I'll take the cable car to the top of the Rock –

have a look at those Barbary apes or whatever they're called, then take a slow walk back to the hotel, collect the motor, drive to the border. Wait.

A cable car is about to set off for the top, I get on, stand by the window. I've not got a head for heights. These days, I've not got a head for lows. I can see the taut cables and the blue sky beyond. I think of the girl and how she'd love to be with me now on her way to see the monkeys, maybe even feed them. I know I should be back in Belfast in a black taxi on my way to Malone Park to beg and plead for her and the wife's return. But I'm not. I'm in a cable car on my way to look at some mangy monkeys shitting and pissing on a rock that's one of the last outposts of the British fucking Empire. No-one knows I'm here. Except your man. Your man knows. Your man always fucking well knows. Fucking gobshite.

Kilburn, March 2008
I didn't notice until now – just goes to show how bollocksed I was last night – but Tony only has four teeth – upper ones. His mouth looks like a neon advertisement for TEETH but with one blinking out so it reads TEE H. The rest of his mouth is a purple hollow where the tongue freely fucking roams. While I'm thinking this, Tony is asking me a question. I don't quite catch all of it, say, Sorry, fella, what was that? I need to get this over with. Fucking eejit I was last night, shooting my mouth off. Getting old. Michael, I say to myself. Past it. I said tell us about the funeral again. The second one, Tony says. Ach, it was a long time ago. I can't remember. You remembered last night, right down to the make ah the underpants those army guys was wearing. Ah, fellas, I say. An old man's imagination. I was there or thereabouts but had nothing to do with the goings on. I was home with my feet up by the fire with the wife and girl. Thought they'd buggered off by then, says Tony. Done a runner to

her parents, that's what you said. You said you'd gone round, kicked the door in, threatened to kneecap her old man if he didn't let you see your daughter. That's what you said. An old man's dreams, it was the drink talking. I'm mixing up things that happened and things I'd like to have happened. Do you never daydream, lad? Oh, I daydream, pops. I daydream all the time – house in the country, yacht, gorgeous bird. But I don't think it's real. I don't go down the pub and tell everyone I meet I'm a fucking millionaire. Tony, fellas, I've got to be going. Mrs. Quinn will have my guts for garters if my food is spoiled. She'll be wondering where I've got to. Thirty seconds and I'll let you go, Tony says, it's just been bothering me since last night. Not you going on about the cause and the old country – I dunno why all you bastards don't fuck off back there, you go on about it so much. No, it was that last thing you told us. I'll start. You interrupt if I'm wrong. I hear footsteps coming from out back and see Jane behind the bar, the barman whispering in her ear. She looks at me and mouths, All right? I half shake my head, half nod. My stomach feels hollow, not sure if it's because of this fella not six inches from my face or the fact that I need to get some air, go to the bookies, eat some food. Tony says, Second funeral you'd been to that week. First one, some nutter shoots the fucking thing up – some balls he must've had – he kills three people but he was aiming for that geezer who looks like a bearded ferret – Adams, that's right – and so the next funeral for one a them that got shot, two army guys are spotted by the crowd – including you – and you chase 'em, corner 'em, drag 'em out of their motor, drive 'em to a sports ground – very fucking sporting – where you strip 'em, torture 'em, throw 'em over a wall – brave, brave – drive 'em in a taxi to some wasteland and then some a you – and you didn't say who, no matter how many drinks I bought you, I'll give you that – some a you shoot and knife the poor fuckers and leave their bodies rotting in puddles, I think you said.

I was just telling you a bit of history, lads. Nothing more. I go to get up but Tony puts his hand on my chest. I can feel my heart thump. I begin to sweat. Jane says, You OK, Michael? About time you were getting home, love, innit? You're probably right, I say. Jane says, You fellas want another or are you on your way? Tony looks at me, his lips thin, pursed. We're OK, he says. Just having a chat with Michael about old times. Seems he's a bit confused. That, or we got the wrong end of the stick, like. Jane says, I'll walk you down the street, Michael. It's on my way. Tony and the others leave. What was all that about? Jane says. Were they in here last night? Aye, I say. Let my gob and my imagination run away with me. Learned my lesson. You're too old for that, you old sod, Jane says. Come on. We leave. Tony and the others are outside, leaning on a car, arms folded, watching the pub. Jane takes my arm. We walk along the High Road. I forget to call in the bookies to check my bets.

Gibraltar, March 1988

The apes doss around, lazy and waiting for food, staring, baring their teeth. They're not apes at all, it says in the brochure, they're monkeys, macaques to be precise. Like most Irishmen. Not Irish at all, half-English, half-Scots, half-bloody-Spanish some of 'em. To tell you the truth, the monkeys are better looking, harder working. I'll have to remember this one to tell the girl – what language do the Gibraltar monkeys speak? Gib-berish. Get it? Ach, I'm kidding. I stroll around for a bit, look at the view – the sea, Africa. Pillars of fucking Hercules. I check my watch, take the cable car back down to the Grand Parade, walk back to the hotel, collect my car, drive to the frontier. Gibraltar – a UK overseas territory. So's the fucking six counties, mind. The neutral zone. Then La Linea – Spain – the way home. Back to what? I get to the frontier at midday, find a café with a good view. Not much is happening apart from a stream of people crossing the border, planes landing at the airport. No added security as far as I can tell. I order a cold drink, position my chair so I can look out the window, pretend to read my book. Pretend. That's what I'm always doing. Pretend to be a husband. Pretend to be a father. Pretend to give a shite about the cause when all it is is a means to an end but what that fucking end is I'll never be sure. My end – Michael O'Connor – big man. Irish Republican Army volunteer. Seen things that would make you sick to your stomach. Make your knees wobble – if you had any left. But this is it. After this, I'm out. Whether the wife and girl come with me or not. Ach, they will. Maybe I won't catch that return flight. Maybe I'll drive up into the mountains. Visit Granada – the Alhambra Palace. Then drive on through Spain. Stop off in Barcelona. Visit a few civil-war sites – Jarama, Ebro, finish off in Guernica. I wonder if those mad Basque bastards are still around. Then drive into France, call the wife and girl from there, ask them to come over – the wife knows where the money is. Stay in a little village – drink wine, take the girl horse riding. There's loads of churches in France – the wife loves churches. Lourdes is just over the Pyrenees – we could meet there. That would be a fucking miracle. What I can't understand is why the Brits didn't come for me sooner. All they had to do was stick a few plainclothes boys on me, follow me for a day; they'd have seen me meeting with known fellas in known places. You can't be so thick as to watch me go into a house on Beechmount Avenue, walls painted with murals of an Irishman hand in hand with a member of the PLO, sharing a fucking rocket launcher for fuck's sake, or one of James Connolly staring out at you from between the tricolour and the starry fucking plough. Why wait until I'd decided to get out? Why kick my door down in front of the wife and girl? Shove me to the ground. Filthy fucking boots on my face. I could hear the wife and girl crying in the kitchen. Then they hooded me – right there in my own home, tied my arms behind my back, carried me out to the fucking Saracen. Drove me somewhere. Those cold brick walls – that fucking chair. They kept me hooded. The odd drop of water. No food. I lost track of time. Thought I'd been there a day. I'd been there three. The fella who questioned me had an Irish accent – Dublin, maybe – but I could hear English voices as well, in the background, just out of reach. I wasn't allowed to sleep, or piss. They soaked the hood with water. I couldn't breathe. Choking. Gagging. Suffocating. I said nothing. Then the whispering started. In my ear. Close up. Intimate. About your man. About the wife. About the girl. He kept it up for hours. I'm not sure if there was one or two of them. Soft voice. Soft voices. While you were gone, Michael. Soft. While you were in America. Whisper. Why do you think they make you run errands? Softer. Out of Belfast a lot, aren't you, Michael? Whispering. Where to next? Voice. Palestine? Voices. When it was all over, when they stopped with the whispering, the voices, they drove me to waste land not far from the house. The Saracen stopped. I could hear the engine running, the doors opened, I felt a shove, a kick on my back. I was on the floor still hooded, my hands untied. The Saracen pulled away. I tore off the hood. Sobbing, spit running down my chin, snot in my mouth, my eyes red, streaming. I groped my way back to the house. I knocked. The house was unlit. I saw curtains twitch in the houses opposite. They'd changed the lock. They'd changed the fucking door. They were gone.

JOHN KING INTERVIEW

John King is the author of seven published novels; *The Football Factory*, *Headhunters*, *England Away*, *Human Punk*, *White Trash*, *The Prison House* and *Skinheads*. He also runs a publishing house with friend, fellow author/Chelsea supporter, Martin Knight. London Books has published new fiction and non fiction, but the jewel in their crown is definitely the republishing of many lost London classics by the likes of Gerald Kersh, Simon Blumenfeld, James Curtis, John Sommerfield and Robert Westerby. Joe England met with John in Battersea during the midst of the World Cup and they shared quite a few beers, the early evening sunshine, but more importantly – the words you are about to read.

JE: You've had much success, especially with your first novel and the subsequent film and you could have milked the media limelight big time with some style and credibility, but you didn't and never have, and that's something I think is very noble. Why is that the case?

JK: I don't think it's conscious, it's your personality really, and I think especially people who become authors are a little bit introverted if you like, alone with their thoughts a lot, and I think that's one of the good things about being an author is that you can be anonymous. I write books because I love writing and I would feel quite embarrassed by that sort of stuff, with that kind of attention. It's just not me. I've never had much interest in that side of it. I'm quite private, have my close friends and like to do what I do. It's just my nature. I'm not what you would call a flamboyant person.

JE: That's refreshing to hear, because some people with zero talent would do anything to be famous these days and some of your characters are definitely not introverted. I read somewhere that you mentioned how it wasn't books but the likes of The Clash and the Sex Pistols who gave you a literary education and a lot of people can relate to that. But what kind of books did you read when you were young, when you were at school?

JK: I used to read the Richard Allen skinhead novels, *Skinheads, Suedehead, Boot Boys,* and all the rest of them, think there was about eleven or twelve. I actually also used to read Agatha Christie books and the Confessions series; *Confessions of a Window Cleaner* and all that stuff. So that was my reading when I was young and the skinhead books, the Richard Allen books, because I was interested in those kinds of subjects. I was into football and music and the culture around me, what they'd call subculture now, and yeah I used to read them and used to think even as a kid they weren't that good, after all they were written by an outsider. But the Confessions books were often quite funny.

JE: These were the books I remember that got passed around the playground, especially the Confessions books. But perhaps not the Agatha Christie ones!

JK: Kevin Williamson used to read the Agatha Christie books too and we used to talk about that. And I wonder about that idea of having that kind of ending that suddenly comes at you, if I ever got any of that from Agatha Christie.

JE: I really enjoyed *Human Punk* when it came out. Clearly John King style, but a totally different landscape and narrative to the previous three novels and such a striking scene in the opening of that kid getting his head sprayed in gold paint on a boiling hot day. Was that event something you witnessed and put into fiction or were you actually that kid who got done in?

JK: No, wasn't me. But there was a kid who got sprayed last day of term. I didn't actually see it, got told about it. Only his head got done. Not like in the James Bond film where the woman gets killed, sprayed in gold paint from head to toe. Not sure if the James Bond film came out before or after that incident.

JE: What I like about the book, is that for anyone who remembers the early years the book's set in, all the bands you mention, the football, then you really get it. The book travels in language, time and place. One moment Joe Martin's in Slough being confronted with the potential death of his mate, then he's in China being confronted by a threatening gang, Speak Chinese Speak Chinese. You get that isolation of him being alone, so far from home. You describe and draw the reader in brilliantly. And then all of a sudden something – maybe insignificant to some – hit my memory bank. It was when you mention *The Big Match* on a Sunday and how *The World At War* was always on before it. I forgot all about that.

JK: See that's my theory about football hooliganism in the 1970s. You had all these kids who were basically the children of people who fought in the war. And on the telly you had war followed by football. And yeah, while I was writing *Human Punk* it was about going back and remembering that kind of stuff, and I drew on a lot of experience, with travelling as well. I spent a couple of years travelling. So in a way although the novel's not autobiographical, it's the nearest out of all my books.

JE: Before any of your books came out, you had *Millwall Away* published in Kevin Williamson's literary fanzine, *Rebel Inc* and that time, the early 90s, was a very exciting time for new writers. Especially those from Scotland. Even though London based, you seemed to quickly become a part of that rising scene of Alan Warner, Irvine Welsh, Laura Hird etc. So you're based down here, but how did get involved in a mag that was essentially new Scottish writing?

JK: Well, as I said, I'd been travelling for a couple of years, came back in the late 80s and I'd always been interested in fanzines and I'd written for the Chelsea Independent before I went away and so I started a fanzine called *Two Sevens* with a friend, Pete Mason, and it was a mix of music, literature, politics, so we had that going. And I don't know where I picked up a copy of *Rebel Inc* from, possibly Compendium Books in Camden, or maybe Kevin had picked up *Two Sevens*, but we ended up getting in touch. Then I think I reviewed *Rebel Inc* in *Two Sevens* and Kevin used to say to me how I should go up there and do an event. But like I say, I was not someone who really did that. But we used to exchange writing. And I think that I did the first ever Irvine Welsh interview for *Two Sevens*. Or certainly one of the first ones.

JE: Tell us more about *Two Sevens*. How did it come about, how big was it, where did you sell it, promote it?

JK: It was an A4 size, we did eight issues in the end. Me and Pete talking about fanzines one day and thought we'd do one. We both liked The Clash, thought about the spirit of 77, and there was the Culture album *Two Sevens Clash*, so there was the name and we just sort of put it together. We tried to sell it in shops, Compendium Books and places like that. Had some distribution through AK Press. Sold it outside some gigs. But it was actually quite hard to sell to a music crowd, harder than a football crowd I guess. But it was good fun. I don't know the maximum of how many we sold, perhaps it was three or four hundred in the end. I have always loved fanzines. Football, literary and music fanzines are the proper alternative press. Because people do it because they love it. And I think that'll always be a great thing.

JE: You mentioned you had Irvine featured, who else was in it?

JK: *Two Sevens* was a real mix. We interviewed the likes of Stewart Home, Steve Ignorant, Leatherface, Alice Nutter, Dennis Bovell, and there were opinion pieces and features – hunting, the meat industry, vivisection, politics generally. Our reviews focused on fanzines and alternative-press material, bands ranging from Fugazi to Spiral Tribe. We included a bit of fiction, some poetry. We had regulars – a Hooligans page, Short Sharp Shocks, a cartoon called The Equalizer. It was a proper mash-up of ideas. No limits. Whatever interested us.

JE: Was *Rebel Inc* the first place you had your writing published?

JK: It was. And it was the only thing printed before I had my first book published.

JE: We're heading into talking about that particular book. But what had you written before then?

JK: When I came back from travelling I thought I was going to be Jack Kerouac. I went and wrote this massive book about travelling. 198,000 words!

JE: That must have helped shape a discipline to completing the books you'd go on to write?

JK: Yeah, for sure. But I think it was also about finding a voice. Before punk came I always felt that there should be a music scene that reflected the life that I knew and something sung in an English accent. And punk fulfilled that and at that time I thought there should be published literature like that. And I was also starting to read more serious books around that time, and I always had it in my mind one day to write something. But when you're young you put it aside because of work, drinking, you go to football, that sort of life. And so I had these ideas, and I was working in a warehouse and I started writing some stuff, kind of futuristic, let that go, then tried the travel story when I came back, and then let it go too. It's a confidence thing isn't it? So I had all these ideas but it was when I got into my thirties I thought, fuck it, I've got to try and do this.

JE: What was the spark for *The Football Factory*?

JK: It was many different things. And the book isn't really about football. It is a microcosm of society. But going to football myself, all the energy, having a drink, loving football, having gone abroad for England games and knowing people from different clubs, and realising that, all that side of it is about the creation of an enemy, like an excuse. It went back to Orwell – the division of people, and the power of the proles if they were united, and it connected with the political system not representing ordinary people. And with the older characters, who to me are the main characters, like Bill Farrell, these were loosely modelled on friends of my dad's, who'd been in the war. When I was fifteen/sixteen, down the pub Sunday lunchtime, you'd have these real heroes with their history, and they're the real core of the book for me and then you had these young lads who wanted to live up to that. And so with the rivalry, football is a continuation of that.

JE: So you got hold of this idea, did you then write it all with some momentum or put together over a period of time?

JK: I did write it as a whole but it wasn't very good and then I wrote it again and I sent it into the editor who eventually took me on but he did say you need to work on this some more and so I worked on it some more and he took it on.

JE: You thank Kevin Williamson and Irvine Welsh in *The Football Factory* for their encouragement. How much did they help you get the book completed?

JK: I think the encouragement was more of being around those people and of course Irvine gave me the quote, which was great, and I think there was a solidarity that goes with the encouragement. Because when you try to write you are always filled with doubts. Doesn't matter how old you are, you are always filled with doubts about writing. Because you are putting your ideas out there. And so when people actually encourage you it's a massive boost. Because you can tell when someone does like what you're doing, because they will pick up on things, even question why certain things didn't happen in a certain way and you know they've read it. I didn't really know many people who read a lot of books. A lot of blokes don't read books do they? I admired what they had going on up in Scotland and it was all good for me too. Because there wasn't really the same thing down here. In the end I was lucky enough to get the book accepted.

JE: Also about timing. There was a new literary scene happening back then. It has always been hard getting a book published; great books are rejected every single day of the week. Do you think in the current climate it is harder for new fiction writers to break through now, more than ever before?

JK: Yeah. One hundred per cent. I got friendly with Alan Sillitoe, he was someone I started to read in my late teens and I got know him in 1999. We published *A Start In Life* for his eightieth birthday. And I met him with my London Books partner, Martin Knight, and we basically all became good mates and we used to meet up fairly regularly, and I said to him one day that it must have been so hard when he first got started, and he said no, it was a lot easier back then than now. He said back in the late 1950s and 1960s there were publishers with money who really believed in literature. So they weren't controlled by accountants. And I reckon it was one hundred times easier when I first got published in the nineties than it is now. Because now everything is about money and profit, accountants and marketing.

JE: You must then think to yourself would the likes of *Trainspotting, The Football Factory* get a look in today?

JK: *The Football Factory* was the first book to deal with that kind of theme in fiction but I don't think it would be published now and *Trainspotting*, well there's actually always been a lot of published drug related fiction, but the book's not really about drugs in my opinion. It was about what Thatcherism did to a community and written with very strong dialect so I don't think that would get published either. And I reckon there must be loads of really good books out there struggling at the moment.

JE: Have to agree with that, has to be the case. Anyway, to finish with *The Football Factory*, Nick Love made a very successful film of the book and Tommy Johnson is a completely different character to the one I read in the novel. Danny Dyer was not how I pictured Tommy. But the film was a great success, albeit on a different level. Nick Love introduced a paranoid drug psychosis angle in

Tommy and new invented characters like Zeberdee. What did you think of his manipulation/adaptation of your book?

JK: Well it was all quite a long process and I was involved in it for a long time, trying to get people interested, and when the book first came out someone else had bought the rights. I first met Nick in the late nineties, and we tried to develop *Headhunters*, my second book, and he wrote a couple of screenplays for that. And although things didn't progress I eventually got Vertigo Films interested in *The Football Factory* and I did an early screenplay and then things evolved and moved on. Nick then came back in as director and he wrote a new screenplay and I think it's a really good film and I'm pleased with it. Especially as the characters are likeable and anyone who knows that world, the football world, is going to feel okay about it. Obviously it is different from the book and yeah Tommy Johnson is more easygoing and there's not the obvious politics of the book in the film, but there are elements that come through in various different ways.

JE: The book was also adapted for the stage. Was it truer to the book?

JK: Theatre is completely different to film. The play was great and yes, closer to the novel. Through it I became very friendly with one of the actors, Steve North. He ended up as one of the producers on the film and was the one who connected me with Vertigo. He has written a screenplay for *Human Punk*, which he will direct. We're trying to get the money together, but it takes time. A lot of authors just sell their work, but I could never do that as it relates to what you are doing as a writer. Film is interesting in its own right, but as an author, to get something out of it and feel happy, you have to try and push your ideas through. Steve's a friend, understands the story that drives *Human Punk*, and I feel easy working with him.

JE: I think I relate, as others I know do, to nearly all of your writing. And I guess I put that down to the fact that you write very well about London and the satellite towns that orbit London and the people that exist within these towns. You do seem to have always had a real sense of purpose in giving a voice to the marginalised/stereotyped white English person. In politics right now certain parties are exploiting this for their own benefit. I know this is a sort of broad open point to raise here, but what are your thoughts?

JK: For me, it is just a case of writing about my life and the things I see and witness, what I feel and believe in. Since I was a young kid, the mass English population has been dismissed and belittled. So everything I was interested in, whether it was football, different forms of music, youth culture, social history, it was always belittled, but that's my culture and so I write about my culture. So for instance with *Skinheads* people were saying, why don't you write about extreme far right wing politics, and I said, why should I? What's that got to do with my book? It's the story of a family who happen to like a particular type of music. It is a story about people. Their struggles. And it links to how the political parties say they represent us but really they don't. They misrepresent us. And I've tried to look at it in a non-party way, and to look at the issues raised on their own merits. Politics has changed so much in my lifetime. What the Tory party is, what the Labour party is. Now politicians are basically all careerists with a fake liberal agenda, while to my mind they are dismantling our democracy. I'm very anti European Union, I see it as a dictatorship in the making. And so this is the rubbish we have in charge today. But if you go back, the politics that were around when I was a kid, well, there was a clear separation between the right and the left. I know people who vote Tory, people who vote Labour, and people with more extreme views on both sides. So for me it's about trying to see the common ground. Because I believe there is a lot of common ground. It's like Margaret Thatcher. She was elected with a big vote. And this wasn't a small middle class victory, she had a big working class vote.

There were plenty of working people who believed the left was communist dominated, anti-British, plus the self employed were being heavily taxed under Labour. I don't like Thatcher, think she did massive damage to this country, but I know people who disagree with me and yet we have common ground elsewhere. So when I write I include a lot of different elements, don't follow a party line. In *White Trash* for instance, I try and show the value of every person, every single person no matter what age they are, what background they come from. *White Trash* is a defence of the NHS. I am pretty patriotic, care about my culture, hate seeing the welfare state being dismantled. I really do believe that everyone has got an equal value. I feel that the majority have been betrayed, want to challenge the myth, the stereotype, that the English are reactionary and racist and all the rest of the lies that have been heaped on us over the years.

JE: You convey some of this point I think in *England Away*. Contradicting the stereotype. The end scene where Tommy see's these two much older English men, a graphically violent scene, but I think a very powerful one on so many levels, he see's these two wankers battering this young German kid, jumping on his head, about to kill him, and they steam over and beat up these two old English blokes, who are in shock, like what the fuck is going on? We're on your side and you draw a parallel in how just like in war you get psychos/cowards/bullies who are there to pick off the stragglers, these guys are never at the front at football, and they are the torturers in a war scene. Because we know Tommy is a violent person, it was such a powerful point to make at the end of the book.

JK: He's an honourable man.

JE: He certainly is.

JK: And as the trilogy goes, *The Football Factory* is people fighting each other, for fun basically, but then at the end of that book he stands back as someone, a Derby fan from an England game he's got to know, gets cornered over at Chelsea by his mates. Then *Headhunters* is about the so-called sex war, but there isn't a sex war because you have got more in common with a woman from your own background than a bloke who isn't. In *England Away* those ideas come together, and there's this thing where people from different clubs become united, they get on, and club loyalties are generally forgotten, and so you get the new enemy who is the foreigner, but you overcome that as well, because everyone is a human being, almost everyone is okay when you get to know them.

JE: And that is why you're writing works. I loved *England Away*. Out of all your books, I read that in one hit. But there is one other book I particularly enjoyed over the rest. That was *The Prison House*. I'd read Brian Keenan's brutal recount of his kidnapping and incarceration in Beirut in *An Evil Cradling*, and it was harrowing, you're inside the mind of someone having the absolute worst kind of living nightmare, the insanity, you're there right in that moment with him, the blackness of the cell, seeing with him what is in his mind, heart of darkness etc, and then here we had *The Prison House* by John King.

JK: I think that book and *Human Punk* are the best I have written.

JE: I agree. Again, with *The Prison House*, you get drawn in there, you smell the fear and the stench from that fucking horrible place. Where did that all come from?

JK: Well, it's a book about incarceration and redemption, but also about the power of dreams, the importance of imagination. How you can survive a terrible situation if you have dreams and imagination. In the book Jimmy creates other worlds and I think people do this generally, but Jimmy is more conscious and focused. There are so many people with strong imaginations who are stifled from expressing them in these ways. Those who control the means to take writers, musicians, etc, to another level, often have limited imaginations, yet they are in these positions of power due to their backgrounds. *The Prison*

House is densely written, but hopefully it works. The style is one of the directions I'd like to go with in my books. It was always a novel I wanted to write. A book without dialogue. It's all internalised. I wrote that early draft in blocks. I enjoy writing like that. You write fast but you have to go back in and really edit it to make it flow.

JE: It works. Those blocks in your books are really intense but when you come out the other side it's like exiting a tunnel into daylight. Let's talk about how you are now a publisher, let's talk about London Books. Your partner in crime is Martin Knight. Are you lifelong friends?

JK: I met Martin just after *The Football Factory* was published and he was involved in *The Working Man's Ballet* with Alan Hudson and though we'd both been going to Chelsea for years, we'd never met, and then we did, and we got on, stayed in touch, became good mates.

JE: And he has brought out a few very good books. You did the forward for *Hoolifan*.

JK: Yeah and he did Peter Osgood's biography, Charlie Cooke's, a book with George Best. He's written some brilliant fiction, like *Common People*, and so we were reading great old London books and had this idea about bringing them back out. I approached a couple of publishers, but with no joy, and one night we were in The Falcon, just down the road from here, and we thought, why don't we just do it ourselves. So we were thinking about a name as a publisher, then one of us said, what about London Books, and it was like fuck off, but we looked into it and no-one had the name. We became London Books. So that was where we started from and we put some money in. The way we wanted to do it, was most of these writers had been out of print for fifty, sixty years, and all that remained was some tatty old paperbacks, and there was very little known about the authors or the books, so we thought about it and what we decided to do was publish in hardback, with colourful and vibrant sleeves, in-depth introductions from contemporary writers. Another thing we did was we reset all the type. If you look at a lot of the big publishers who put old books out, they just photocopy the text. There's no love there. It's much harder work and costs money to reset, and that's why they don't do it, but we want to give these books maximum respect. We work hard and put it all together and we both got it going and we're both bloody minded about it all and we're going to do this until all the shops have got them! We're a very small publisher. We have a distributor, we don't have an individual sales person and it's hard to get the books into shops, hard to make them work financially, which they don't. But over time, what we'd like to do – and we've already published a couple of new novels – we'd love to get a new fiction list up and running. Just need the money.

JE: You published fiction by Peter Haynes, or Esso out of The Lurkers as some like me still know him by.

JK: Yeah, *Malayan Swing*, a fantastic novel. That's the sort of material I believe is out there. But for now, we just do a couple of books a year. We work with freelancers, two really good people, and we've published some great novels together, but now it's all about making that next step, getting decent money so we can increase production.

JE: The look of the London Books Classics series are as brilliant as they are to read. Same with the Rebel Inc Classics. Very iconic covers.

JK: We take the look as seriously as the writing. We wanted to do something different, and the idea was to make it very clean, very modern. I don't think these books feel dated, not when you read them now. The writing is totally alive.

JE: I've just finished *There Ain't No Justice* by James Curtis and the authentic language of the book *is* alive, but like you just said earlier, the introductions are just as important, a clear persuasion why you should read the book and also question why these books were ever allowed to go out of print. But even though there is violence in some of the books, like in your writing, the humanity angle prevails. And not many people get that. They don't look beyond the violence in the writing.

JK: Well the thing is, violent people don't generally write books. Like in music. The less-violent thinkers listened to aggressive punk while the nutters went to discos. The real nutters weren't the punks. It was the soul boys. But anyway, some people might say the Curtis books are pulp, but I don't agree at all. For me, being interested in London, the culture of London, all the varying parts, they are social documents. You get a book like John Sommerfield's *May Day* set in the East End in the 1930s, Simon Blumenfeld's *Jew Boy* set in Petticoat Lane, and I can remember getting the tube from Uxbridge up to Aldgate, then going up Petticoat Lane in the seventies when you had the Last Resort shop there, and I can relate to all that, make the connections. In *There Ain't No Justice* you've got Shepherd's Bush and Notting Hill before it was gentrified, and then there's the Soho novels of Robert Westerby and Gerald Kersh. These books connect to places where I know, that I am interested in, pubs I've drunk in, the streets and markets and so on. Much of that London is gone, the people squeezed out, but they recover and re-establish themselves in the suburbs and new towns. Inner London has whole districts that have been rebuilt and sold off overseas now. No character or culture. Again, it's all about money. There is no interest in community. None.

JE: All roads lead to Thatcher. There's no such thing as society.

JK: One hundred per cent. Our controllers are busy selling everything off to the highest bidders.

JE: You have a small bio at the back of the Gerald Kersh book, *Night And The City*, where you also wrote the introduction, and there's mention that you were currently writing a novel called, *Angel Dust*. Now that was in 2007 and for a man who was been prolific and put out, seven books in eight, nine years, that's a big downswing in momentum. And I am asking this because a few of my contributors have asked me to ask: when's the next John King book coming out?

JK: Well, my dad got ill, very ill, was in and out of hospital, had a heart operation, didn't recover. It took a long time before he died and I helped look after him for several years, and so I couldn't write, didn't want to write. It knocked me back for a long time. But *Angel Dust* has become *Slaughterhouse Prayer* and that's a book that I've finished now. And it's being read at the moment. It's to do with animal rights, comes from the point of view of a vegan. So it's quite a contentious book if you like. It's about a character who when he's young he thinks his prayers will save the animals – because when he is very young he finds out where meat comes from. So he thinks wishful thinking and prayers will save them. When he is in his late teens, early twenties, he thinks words can stop the slaughter. If he can articulate things, protest peacefully, that'll save them. But when he comes to middle age, he realises nothing is going to change, so he decides he has to take direct action. Direct violent action. And so he's a soldier, and he legitimises what he is going to do. As a soldier you go in, you do the job, don't take any pleasure in killing. That is the theory. So what he starts to do is kill people in the meat industry and dairy industry. He starts with a couple of workers at a slaughterhouse, he shoots them, and nothing much happens as a result. And then it all escalates. He works his way up the pecking order, to the advertising industry, the people that own the factories. But what he is trying not to do, is take pleasure from his actions. But is that possible? So you have that question and it links into a lot of themes I have written about before. This is what drives *Slaughterhouse Prayer*. I have researched the mechanics of slaughter, the use of language, been a vegetarian for thirty years, a vegan for a long, long time. So I know what it is all about.

JOHN KING
The Terror Fantastic

The men were drinking and so their mood was changing. It was Friday night and the working population was clocking off and celebrating their freedom in the traditional manner, but these two had been sacked from their jobs killing chickens and removed from the flow. Their anger, which had sunk into defeatism earlier, was rising up again and reshaping as defiance and a growing sense of injustice. When an elderly regular made a remark about their cruelty he was asking for trouble.

Nerve of the smelly old cunt standing there wanting to know if they were proud of themselves tormenting those poor birds. Poor birds? Fucking cheek. All puffed up like a rooster who didn't realise he was going to get his throat cut and head sliced clean off so he could run around in circles kicking skinny little legs and flapping featherless wings. Horrible fucker telling them they should be bloody ashamed torturing defenceless animals. His friends were sitting at a nearby table, nodding their heads like brainless hens, admiring their cockerel, a fancy boy strutting about not seeing he was about to put on a show for the lads. Pensioners tapping and tutting their tongues, and the bigger of the two cutters told them it was only their age saving them from twenty stitches each. He had his tools with him and there would be no stunning tonight. Really, it was the law protecting these men from a dose of what they'd given the birds, what other slaughterers were dishing out to lambs and pigs and cows at this very moment.

Ricky Spears hadn't known how to respond at first, standing behind Bob Cummings who he knew wasn't going to let himself be told off like he was a kid. Bob had his say, finished the last mouthfuls of lager and cradled the empty glass in the palm of a huge right hand as if he was about to shove it in the bloke's face, leaning in close and leering, telling the decrepit old donkey that he bet he liked his chicken when it was roasted. Nice bit of breast. Crispy legs that were easy to snap. Deep-fried wings covered in breadcrumbs. Didn't ask too many questions when he was down the supermarket searching the freezers for a bargain and didn't turn his nose up when his Sunday dinner was being served either, did he? No. Of course not. It's got nothing to do with you. We were having some fun. Goes on all the time. And I hope you get cancer and die. The man went red in the face and returned to his friends, who stood up and left the pub. Go on, fuck off.

Ricky was elated, just wished Bob had used the glass, the spite that drove him following the men out into the street as he imagined himself trailing the big mouth who'd done the talking until he was on his own, battering him with a brick as he reached his front door. He would take the key and drag the man inside. Ransack the place. Find a hidden fortune in cash. All sorts of valuables. Ricky flushed as he thought about the pain he could inflict if only he had the courage to stab at that neck with a blade, wished the law would let him kill prisoners like those jihadis he saw on the TV, wanted to live in the sort of society where he could wear a uniform and hurt his enemies at will. He would tie the geriatric to a chair, smooth out those crinkly features with a kettle of boiling water. Embarrassing them like that in public.

It had been bad enough going to court and being written about in the local paper, and then one of the big boys picked up on the story and plastered their faces and names all over a national. This made him edgy. It wouldn't be hard for the animal-rights mob to find out where he lived. He wasn't big and strong like Bob, but he did have brains, and this made him more wary than his friend.

It was a shame he'd lost that job. There was plenty of overtime and as long as he planned ahead, he could more or less choose his hours. What was going on in the world when people like him and Bob were sacked and fined for having a laugh with animals that were going to die soon anyway? It was mental. Made no sense. Those chickens were rotting inside and out, covered in lumps and sores, their bodies loaded with hormones, riddled with disease, knees inflamed and creaking. Mucky little cunts pissing and shitting everywhere. Timid and petrified. Pathetic. The din these birds made was incredible, but nobody on the outside heard them screaming so nobody came to help. There was no escape. He was God in that place. His balls tingled.

He remembered a photo he'd seen of a young Ozzy Osbourne sitting with a cock's head, fag in its mouth, like it was puffing away. Glazed dead eyes. Ozzy smirking. Ozzy the slaughterman. Ozzy the hard nut. A rock n roll star. He'd cracked up when he saw that picture, had one of the lads recreate it with Ricky in the driving seat. They'd had a laugh. Him and Bob and one or two others. It was freakshow stuff. Circus sex. Dwarves and clowns. He giggled. The cunt slagging them off was no spring chicken. He wished he'd thought of that line before. Bob would have laughed. They dealt in children. Young meat was best. Headless chickens. Running. Funny as fuck.

He supposed, when he really thought about what his brief had said, they'd had a result of sorts, the toffs presiding letting them off with a slap on the wrist. Truth was, magistrates liked their flesh same as the next person. As the chairman admitted, food production could be a messy business, but this was work that had to be done. The accused fulfilled a function, kept the system moving, and while Spears and Cummings were clearly of low intelligence and not the sort he would want to associate with personally, they had found their place in society. Ricky was fuming at these comments and, replaying things now, he wished he could cut those magistrates up as well. They were going through the motions, he knew that, had to be seen to apply the law, but there was no need to insult them in that way. It was a con.

As for those animal-rights nutters, well, the drink was increasing his confidence. They preferred damaging property to people. He'd heard about firebombs, smashed windows, but so what? Even though they were looneys, they only went so far, weren't going to turn up and give him a hiding. Most were pacifists. His mate Bob might have been thick, but he'd laughed and dismissed them as peace-loving scum when Ricky mentioned he was worried. Hippies and anarchists and punks and travellers. Called them the Lentil Lovers. Bob was right. Worst they could do was turn up and give them some lip. Bob would deal with that easy enough.

The company itself didn't give a fuck about the birds. They only cared about turning a profit, had said things they didn't believe to cover themselves, like the magistrates and the politicians who made the laws. It was bollocks. Ricky would have to find another job and was going to miss the overtime, had enjoyed the work, felt strong and powerful there, part of a gang, his real mistake letting that dozy cunt Williams film them on his mobile. He was the one who'd stitched them up, putting it on the internet, but at least he'd called and said sorry, that he'd only done it for a laugh. Went and put the name of the firm up there as well though. Their faces couldn't be missed. Complaints were made and the police came knocking. Coppers looking at them as if they were filth.

He sipped his drink and leaned against the bar. Give it three months and he wouldn't be surprised if the firm took them back on, once the fuss had died down. Everyone deserved a second chance. But he needed to work meantime, would try some of the big slaughterhouses maybe. Lambs would be easy. Pigs tough. Bullocks seriously hard. Birds were a doddle. Chickens and ducks. Most of these animals had gone mad, too dumb to break out and make a run for it when they were still sane, like the Jews in the Second World War. How many of them had fought back? At least they'd turned up the pressure in Israel. Look at what they were doing to the Palestinians. Kicking fuck out of the ragheads after stealing their land. Good luck to them as well. That's what it was all about. They did the kosher number on their animals as well. Cut their throats and bled chickens to death without dipping their head in electrified water first. Stunning was a waste of time and effort. Mind you, a lot of animals weren't done properly. No, the Jews didn't fucking bother. Made them suffer. For God. Same as the Muslims. Halal and kosher slaughter. There was no such thing as *humane* slaughter. Ask anyone working on the front line.

Bob was his best pal of the last two years. They'd met at work and had a laugh, bossing the birds about, taking the piss. Bob was slower than Ricky, took time to catch up with his ideas, but he was handy with his fists, short-tempered and easily led, and Ricky liked this – he was the brains and Bob the muscle. They made a good team. He was the general, Bob his soldier. It was like having his own protection squad. Nobody was going to fuck him about when Bob was nearby.

He had to admit he'd been surprised by his mate's anger after the magistrate fined them, hadn't expected Bob to take it the way he had, going on about animals not being alive like humans and how they didn't feel pain. It had started to get on Ricky's nerves after a while, but he kept quiet, let him ramble on. Ricky knew he was wrong about the chickens and ducks and all the rest of them not experiencing pain. If they were objects who felt nothing, where would be the fun in hurting them? You didn't torture a carrot did you? Why would comedians bother telling jokes? There was no point if the animals weren't scared. Deep down he was sure Bob knew the truth, otherwise he wouldn't have joined in. Their terror really was fantastic to see.

Bob was trying to chat up the barmaid now, a fat cow with udders for tits, but he was slurring his words and Ricky reckoned she was disgusted with them, same as the old man. That slag needed a good seeing to and he pictured Bob taking her out round the back of the pub and fucking her good and hard. That would sort her out. Ricky watched his mate spluttering into his pint, but the time was passing and the pub would be emptying out soon and he was suddenly very tired. It has been a tough week and his head was starting to ache. He needed some fresh air. The barmaid went off to collect glasses and he suggested they leave. Bob shrugged. He'd had enough and so they went out into the night and strolled away, ambling along the streets and taking the lane next to the recreation ground, down past the boarded-up toilets. Moonlight turned the grass a deep yellow. The trees ahead were black and dense. It was a peaceful night.

The two friends continued in silence. Ricky was relaxed. Life wasn't so bad. He had money coming from his work and some savings, would maybe go away for a week or two before looking for a new job. He had his eye on the latest iPhone, had been meaning to upgrade, could splash out on that, but he reasoned that some time away would be a better use of the money. People quickly forgot. A fortnight off the radar and who would still be thinking about a few headless chickens? They didn't care. Not really. He had a brother living by the sea who would put him up if he asked, but better than that would be a holiday in the sun. Spain and Greece offered some decent two-week packages. He could ask Bob to go with him, but he would be better on his own. First night he would meet a woman in his hotel bar and spend the days swimming and going on the odd excursion, drinking and eating his nights away. She would be a good-looking blonde who loved dishing out blow jobs. This woman would fall in love with him instantly and do whatever he wanted. She would have plenty of cash and buy him that iPhone as a present. He didn't want a zero-hours girl. No fat cows who worked in pubs. He would take pictures of her wearing a red bikini on his new phone, listen to music as he tanned in the sun, come back brave and strong and reborn. He was much more than a survivor. Nobody would be able to touch Ricky Spears as he landed at the airport and was met by Bob who had come to pick him up, and he would be dropped off at his girlfriend's house – she would have left a couple of days before and been badly missing him – and there would be a bottle of Champagne in a bucket waiting and a nice spread and she would look after him while he considered his options, scouted around for a job. There would be no rush. He had done a few things he probably shouldn't have, been found out this time but got away with it, more or less. He grinned. Yes, life was sweet.

There was a rustle in the row of evergreens they were passing, as if a crow was moving through the branches. Crow, raven, eagle. Gravel crunched. Ricky and Bob turned but only saw their attacker as an outline. The man moved fast, came from the shadow cast by the trees.

A length of wood connected with Bob's head and he dropped to his knees. He stayed like this for a few seconds before flopping forward unconscious. Ricky turned to run but panicked and slipped, felt a blow across his back and went down, managed to swivel so he was sitting and looking up at the silhouette standing over him, a leg pulling back and foot zooming in and smashing into his face, sending him sprawling. He raised fingers to his face, touched his nose and groaned, knew that it was broken. He tried to get to his feet but was too weak. His attacker stood still. Faceless. A cricket bat in his right hand.

Ricky was fixed to the ground, his body frozen, knew he was going to die as urine filled his jeans, and it was strong and pungent and took him back to the slaughterhouse, ammonia stinging his eyes as he begged for mercy, reaching inside his jacket and offering up his wallet and the keys to his flat, told the man he could take whatever he wanted, that his mate had cash on him. Keys also. He could write down their addresses. The wallet was kicked away, his attacker dropping the bat and pulling out a knife that flashed in the moonlight, and he moved fast and was down on one knee, grabbing Ricky's hair and yanking it and bending the head sideways so it was resting on bone. The man was strong and powerful and there was no escape. Ricky's neck was exposed and the blade close, steel pressing against the artery, blood flushing past as his heart thumped hard.

Ricky tried to speak but the words were jumbled and he was making no sense, and as he faced death he wished he could flap his wings and rise into the sky and fly away and live out his days in peace, didn't understand how humans could do such terrible things. But his would-be killer paused and in a flash Ricky realised he didn't have it in him. It was a revelation. This cunt could not kill. Ricky was the strong one. He thought of the hamster he'd had as a boy, the dog he had hurt as a teenager and finally strangled when it was old like that cunt in the pub. No, his attacker was a coward. Despite everything, he laughed out loud, lips peeling back as he sneered.

The man pushed him away, stood and retrieved the cricket bat, raised it high and hesitated, then brought it down on Ricky's right knee. He jolted and felt his bowels go, curled into a ball and hid his face, waiting for the next blow, but instead heard footsteps on the gravel, imagined the crowing of a cockerel. He was about to open his eyes but knew people were sneaky and planned ahead, that his attacker might be hovering in the air, free and unrestrained and ready to do more damage, beak sharpened and deadlier than the knife. Ricky tightened the ball he had made with his body, but still nothing happened and he tried to find the courage to look out, finally saw that apart from Bob he was alone.

Ricky tried to stand but his leg was on fire, and he called for help, tears filling his eyes, started to shout out loud, didn't care when he puked up the lager from the pub, could feel the shit and piss on his body and knew he was no better than one of those scabby animals he killed. He was a headless chicken... bleating lamb... smelly pig... dirty fucking cow. The pain was terrible and he was sure he was going to die. He began to cry, softly at first, and then his self-pity was drowning him and he choked, clucking deep in his throat, voice distorting as he screamed and pleaded for someone to come and save him. But nobody heard. And so nobody came.

FORD DAGENHAM

They Launched

doodlebugs above the Thames
overtook the wrens on bicycles
and
scream-dove on iron fins
to
crack East End bells
to black and white photos
trimmed wonky
with
nail scissors in gas light
half-names and guess-dates
written on the backs
in shaky biro
of
glum toad-faces in winter overcoats
standing awkwardly on rubble tumbles
in boxy boots
running
fish shops
between
siren wails

JIM GIBSON

Old Town

'The cinema stood there me lad
spiralling into the sky
With a great banner. Lighting the newest films.
We used to go down once a week,
all of the town would have a peek.
But it wasn't really for what was on screen.'

The bland supermarket car park
Sparsely littered with cars
Made it hard to picture
This described grand fixture

'And over there was the old dance hall,
before they were council flats.
It was buzzing on a Saturday,
it's where I met your granny one night.
Jiving and jigging in the dimly lit light.'

He had a wiggle of his hips
And smiled at me
But I could see the tear in his eye
Now two bedroomed flats
house families of five
With no room for a jig or a jive

'The pubs were different as well.
They weren't just for the weekend.
To get shitfaced around strangers.
We'd nip in for one nearly every evening,

just to say hello and to be seen in.
We'd arrive there and laugh.
Hoot a howl and a swear word,
not ignore everyone,
in front of the boring Spoons waitress.
But be invited to the heart,
of the beer battered temptress.'

I knew he was right

I could feel the warmth in his voice

The homeliness that this town once brung

Before bedroom tax
And supersale to the max
Were the only way to get the bare basics

When people went out for fun

Not up our own arses

Like the adverts, the buzz

And fake cultures employ us.

JON TAIT
Snake Blood Shots

I was working as a package handler for a big international delivery firm. You stood around on the loading dock of the warehouse under a sick yellow sodium strip light in cargo pants and dimpled gloves waiting for the trailers to pull in. They were 50 foot long containers and when you opened the back doors, they were loaded right up tight, floor to ceiling with cardboard boxes. Occasionally you'd swing open those doors and the container would be only half full, but mostly they were jam packed.

Then you had to pull the boxes down and feed them onto a belt of rollers with a heavy push that span them past the driver's individual docks so they could load up for the morning. It was a graveyard shift and a minimum wage gig. And they worked you hard. The sweat would be pouring off by the time you'd pulled and thrown half a trailer and Mick Malone, the driver's boss, would be on your back.

'Can't you handlers go any faster? Fucking hell, it would be quicker doing it myself,' he'd growl.

He had a beat-up face like a boxer and was squat and stocky. A company man. Keen to move up in the business. He could see that I didn't give a fuck and despised me for it.

'Get your arse into gear, Morgan,' he spat, his dark eyebrows frowning over his furious eyes as he barged by and started throwing down boxes. 'Get off the belt and out of my way.'

'No problem, Malone.'

But he'd only last five minutes and then he'd barge past bristling with temper and I'd get back on to heaving the heavier parcels like engine parts and pool tables off the bottom of the floor and watching out for dodgy stacking that was likely to topple down on you.

Mac was an old guy that worked the trailers with me. I went up the left side of the runner belt that ran up the centre of the trailer and he went up the other side. He had greying hair and the work was too heavy for him, but he never complained. His cheeks were red with effort.

'We're nearly there, Morgan,' he'd say as we decimated the load.

But we knew that there would be another twenty trailers pull in after this one and Malone had his goddamn schedule to keep. Never mind if the trailers were late, we still had to have them all unloaded for the driver's arrival to start delivering in the morning.

I went and got a paper cup of coffee from the machine and stood outside in the mist smoking a cigarette between loads. Malone expected us to help load up the driver's bays but fuck him, I thought, I fancied a break. It was the only way to break up the monotony. It was somewhat reassuring that you didn't have to think to do the job. The repetition of the work got you into a groove, a strange Zen-like meditative state. When you were lifting and you didn't have to talk or think, it was strangely comforting.

A young guy stood at the doors scanning the labels on the packets and you just had to make sure that he could zap them with the laser gun. And try not to crush, smash or spill any of the loads. But I needed to roll up some tobacco for a smoke every time we'd done a trailer. It was a reward. I also had a bit of hash in a cellophane wrapper and rolled it in my fingers wondering whether I should crumble some in. The radio was on low and you could barely hear it above the clank and crash of metal cages, men's random singing and coughing and the hum of the lighting.

With it being a graveyard shift, start time was 3am and I struggled to get to work every morning. We were finished by eight and I liked to lay in the bath with a bottle of beer in the morning in the one bedroom flat that I shared with Lucie, a barmaid from one of the nightclubs in town. The warm water splashed over my aching muscles as I sucked down the ice cold lager and played idly with my cock.

Lucie had short hair dyed red, flames and greenish blue eyes flashed intensely like a coal fire was burning behind them when we fucked, her firm tits and juicy pink nipples bobbing as she climbed on top and slid her knickers to the side and slipped me in. Lucie loved to be on top.

We were saving to go travelling in South East Asia. Every week we'd cash our wages and roll some notes away in an old metal tea tin that she kept under the mattress. It was satisfying to see the roll accumulating with dirty, greasy notes, all light blue and brown and purple. It made working with blokes like Mick Malone bearable, the fact that I knew I was going to walk away from the job as soon as we had enough cash. The visions that I had of those jungles and beat-up shanty streets with neon signs and hand painted fascias at wonky angles with tuk-tuks and scooters buzzing through the dust kept me going.

I fell stiffly into the bed, every muscle aching as though I had the flu, and lightly kissed the back of Lucie's neck.

'How was work?' she said dozily without opening her eyes.

I grunted and sucked on her ear lobe.

'Tell me more about Thailand, Lucie – it's all the keeps me going at that place,' I said, my hands gripping her soft arse cheeks.

She gasped and backed onto me.

'There are moonlight raves down on the beach with dancers holding flames,' said Lucie, turning to face me with her smoky blue green eyes. 'But do you know what will blow your mind, Morgan?'

'What?' I asked excitedly.

'In the neon bars along the strip you can get shots of snake blood vodka from Thai girls. It's so hot and exotic, it's like a dream.'

I shook my head in amazement and drifted off to sleep with a grin on my face, just anticipating that flight out to strange new places. I couldn't wait to tell Malone to stick his half-bit job up his arse.

When I awoke in the twisted sheets of the bed, with light streaming in through a gap in the curtains, Lucie was gone. I pulled on my worn jeans and when I went to check the old tea tin under the mattress, well, that was gone too. My heart chilled to ice and Mick Malone's beat-up laughing face invaded my mind.

An Introduction

The following poem – *How Come?* – was written in 1992. It named Leon Brittan as a practicing paedophile in the pages of *Rebel Inc Magazine*, issue 2.

Rebel Inc at the time was a high profile literary publication. No one was sued.

It was well known that Leon Brittan was a paedophile while he was Home Secretary. He was protected by Margaret Thatcher and even after his death, his abominable crimes against children are still protected by the British Establishment.

Kevin Williamson
Edinburgh
July 2015

KEVIN WILLIAMSON

How Come?

how come
Pauline
was locked
up for
six months
for
stealing
baby food
from an
Asda superstore

and how come
Ernest Saunders
was locked
up for
nine months
for
embezzling
five million

and
how come
every editor
in Fleet Street
and politicians
on both sides

and two prime ministers
and the police
and MI5
all know
the real reason
why Leon Brittan
was discreetly
bundled off
to Europe
on the pretext
of Westland
after what
a fireman
found
at a blaze
in a
West London
flat

how come
editors
won't
print it
how come
the police
won't
do nuthin
how come
no arrest
for the
wicked

how come
Pauline
put in jail
and
how come
Ernest Saunders
makes the
worlds
first
successful
recovery
from
senile
dementia

and
how come
Leon Brittan
is still
sliming
all over
Europe
on thousands
of pounds
a week
and not in
Brixton
with the *beasts*

how come, eh
how come?

WAYNE HOLLOWAY
King Bun

Darts is all about mental maths. For the players, the punters and for the bookies. What does he need to go out? What's a players stats for each double, each treble? When to take a bet, when to stop taking bets, when to lay a bet off.

So when Marmaduke Brecon from the Jolly Sailor in Hanworth took on Jim Pike representing the Windmill Club for the News of the World Darts Championship in September 1938, it was all about the sums. Back in the 30's 'in game betting' meant a bookie or his runner taking bets from the home crowd and buying the opposing team drinks, whooping it all up and making a killing. Wet thumbs flicking through the odds, quickly penciled in before the game. 1st leg 180s, highest check-out of the match, odds tumbling as the arrows mount up. More stats to process, the likelihood of every outcome shifting columns invisibly with every throw, every pint sunk. Quick minds recalculating the numbers, and all the while, in the eye of this numerical storm, the players intent on figuring out what they need to go out, eying their favourite doubles, their lucky trebles, in order to win each leg. Keeping a calm head amidst the booze and the barracking when all about you are losing theirs...

Have a bang on that.

August 1938, Bermondsey

Georgie Boy Pallen, tired, his voice hoarse, but a tidy sum stashed deep in his pocket, sets off with an easy gait, his loose-fitting suit sailing him down the street. An uncomplicated nights work, the darts crowd not normally known for violence, so a night without tension, well, with less anxiety, because you never know, even when you know. Right?

Past midnight, three raps with the hand of a street door knocker. Upstairs, a fleshy hand clamps the mouth of a startled awake blonde, followed by up, and an ear to the door, expectant. Next a muffled shout, which sounds like, has the rhythm of...

'Open up, Police!'

Georgie Boy waits downstairs, smiling to himself, gyrating on his own feet, a young man, full of piss and vinegar, playing a prank on his boss with a twinkle in his eye.

Upstairs, older eyes flick over the room, land on the spine of a big black ledger under the bed.

'Fuck me,' Wally mutters to nobody. 'Fuck me!'

He slips on his shoes, grabs the book, wipes the dust off it and chucks it out of the window. He girds himself; fag end flicked on ahead, turns to the bed and shushes the blonde now propped up on one elbow. He winks, before turning back to the window.

'I'm too old for this shit.'

'Wally!' she screams.

He jumps, it's only a single storey, but he catches his foot on the sill and pitches forward. The railings go right through him, through his dirty collared shirt, stuffing his off white vest through his heart.

A big man, his body crumples over at least two posts, stone dead. Pages from the book came loose in flight, and now flutter down the street, wind pasting them up against lamp posts, tucking them away in gutters. Neatly spaced names and numbers filling every page, pencil smudging on contact with the wet gutter.

Georgie Boy sways by the door, chuckles to himself, a half empty bottle of something swinging loose in his hand.

'Open up, Police!' a put-on deep voice, trailing off, wasted as there seems to be nobody in. A last swig, a mumbled, 'Well fuck you Wally!' as he walks off unsteadily into the night, the last we hear of him, the now empty bottle smashing in the gutter.

Under the window, Wally's face has the look of surprise about it. Small details. The street lamp hadn't been working for more than a week. Silent surprise; he isn't found till just before dawn.

The blonde, framed by the window, knows better than to scream. She stifles a sob and disappears.

Local bookie dead. Gruesome end for local character and illegal street bookmaker Red Wally Sasso

Read the headline in the local rag.

'Who pushed Wally the Russian and what for?'

Read everybody's lips.

As if the threat of war wasn't enough to keep people occupied in the stifling heat of late summer. Local news, local celebrity. Tales of everyday life that offered some traction against the inexorable tide of history.

Hitler had nothing on Wally and Georgie Boy that August 1938. In Bermondsey at least, he had a lot of catching up to do.

May 11, 1937

The night before the Coronation, the women were out scrubbing the street. There was going to be a party, so it had to look smart; for the photographer, for the local paper, for the record. Georgie Boy came home to no tea, which pissed him off nearly as much as the fucking Royal family did, his wife a mug like all the rest, so he went straight back out to the pub, muttering to the women he passed that the weather would be shit anyway so why bother.

Pint of stout, glass of port and brandy. Georgie got out his tobacco tin and rolled himself a fag, the concentration calming him. Nobody bothered him when he was rolling.

He lit up, sucked in and opened his paper, breathed out and smoothed it out on the counter. At that moment, before any reading had been done, a small fella sidled up to him.

'Georgie?'

A small hesitant man with a weasel face, a rolled up newspaper under his arm and a pencil in the top left pocket of his cheap suit. The top of the pencil looked wet, bitten. He oozed the nervous energy of your everyday chump.

Smoke haze hangs between them as Georgie takes his time reading the headline:

BUSMEN TO CONTINUE STRIKE

'Yes, bud, what can I do for you?' His fingers tap out on his Players 'No name' tobacco tin.

He flicks the paper over to the back page, taps the headline.

'You hear? Mick the Miller just passed, made a lot of money out of that dog, a lot of money.'

Georgie is whimsical when slightly drunk, 'Mick the Miller' being a famous brindle greyhound who, as he says, had just died. He drains his pint in libation to the dead greyhound, pushes the paper sideways across the bar. The punter stares at it.

'Didn't have you down for a commie, Georgie.'

Georgie sobers, his eyes narrowing with unwanted focus, the little man, the punter, draws back from the line he just crossed. All of this involuntary signs of the times, flickering violence. The moment passes.

'Cayton's the best tipster there is, Commie or not, you're the one should be reading the Daily Worker chump.'

The chump pushes the paper back across the bar, gets down to business.

'Last race of the night, what you give me for Highland Rum?'

'To win? Not a lot to be honest, lot of punters fancy that horse.'

Georgie pulls out his pocket book.

'What about a forecast with Finnegan's Rainbow?'

'Better, can give you 3's, 2 for the reverse.'

'Straight, Highland Rum first.'

Pencil biter hands him a pound note.

Georgie nods, marks it down in his pocketbook. He looks at his watch.

'If you're going to the races I wouldn't wait on a bus, looks like the buggers are on strike.'

He winks, tapping his newspaper.

Georgie gestures for another round as the chump exits, his eyes smiling at that days satirical comic strip, 'King Buns Coronation'.

Later, nearby, Wally's office

Wally sweats over his books. In his late 40s, and for somebody who came late to nutrition, he can already feel a certain dissipation. He stares as a blob of sweat lifts the ink off the page in front of him, magnifying the figures. He dabs at it with his finger, smudging it, making it worse. He pushes back from the desk in disgust and wipes his brow with a handkerchief. Head back, eyes shut, he sits there cooling. Which is how Georgie Boy finds him, momentarily defeated.

'You look like you been shot.'

Wally wipes the hanky from his face, eyes Georgie with his head back, fixing him in the crosshair lines of his face like a WW1 fighter ace.

'Well, they missed. What do you know?'

He sits forward, pulls open the desk drawer, brings out a bottle of vodka and two glasses. From his jacket pocket Georgie pulls out a small fold of notes and a cloth bag of coins, places them on the desk.

'It's all there, average day, not a lot, a quiet one.'

He places the notebook next to the money as Wally pours them two glasses.

'It's the coronation tomorrow, that's what it is. A fucking distraction.'

'And the women want the men to behave all right. Stay home, be sober. Pub was half empty.'

They drink as Wally counts the money and flicks through the notebook.

Georgie looks around the room. Could be a private detectives office, he thinks passively; a desk, standard lamp, dirty window, blinds throwing shadows from the streetlight, some shelves, books. Not that he'd ever seen one except at the Trocette. Ricardo Cortez starring as Sam Spade.

It was always one drink with Wally, never the bottle.

'I bet he's got a gun in that drawer.'

Wally puts the bottle back, Georgie Boy downs his shot, stands up leaning forward, fishing for a glimpse of that revolver. Wally slams the drawer shut and leans back.

It's definitely the blinds, slashing an orange glow across the room that makes it like a private dick's office.

'It will pick up, always does. Soon as things get back to normal.'

Wally is already copying back into his ledger the nights takings. Georgie stares at the book.

'What we need is a bloody revolution. Even the Bolsheviks paid their gambling debts Wally. Remember that?'

'...and you in nappies at the time. You been talking to that kid Rubin again?'

Georgie Boy shrugs.

'The workers have nothing to lose but their gains.'

Wally hands Georgie Boy back his notebook.

'Smart arse that one. Commissar or king, makes no odds son, there will always be pogroms, and this book, this book will burn like all the rest. Goodnight Georgie.'

'Night.'

Georgie has an idea, the booze birthing a thought, a way of fighting back, against what he didn't really care about. He runs down the stairs.

Wally twists his fathers gold signet ring out of habit, gothic letters entwined. It's too tight to twist round his finger, it meets resistance; Fat fingers, fat bulging up over the letters. A ring that in his youth had spent more time in the pawn shop than on his hand, but now he'd have to cut his finger off to pawn it again, so he better not fuck up. All this flashes through his mind for no better reason that Georgie Boy and his smart arse comments stirring up memories, a mind more agile, thank fuck, than his body.

I feel nothing, no identity greater than me, here and now. My kids, wife, work, that's who I am, anything else is a dangerous fantasy, Dad knew that alright, Frederick, Freddy, not even his real name, his Limehouse name he called it, stepping off the boat back in 1921. Got to use it for less than five years.

Wally balls his hands into big baby fists. He blows on the ink, like on a book of spells, pats his head once more with the handkerchief, opens the drawer and from deep inside, past the bottle, he pulls out an old oversized service pistol. He places it on the desk, his hands chasing sweat off opposite palms as he studies it.

'All I need is a commie Jew for a runner.'

A lock-up, round the corner

Round the back of the flats was a lock-up garage. Georgie kept all his old shit in it, since before he got married. An old motorbike, too dirty to keep in the house, blah blah blah, but also other stuff; Georgie had always been good with his hands, mending, making, used to help his dad out at the allotment, built a trellis once for tomatoes and that took a lot of twine, which is what he was fumbling for now, a big ball of the stuff under the work bench in a cardboard box. That and the tin of white paint he never got around to painting the outside bog wall with.

Now it was late, everybody on the street tucked up for the big day. Painstakingly, Georgie Boy, for he was nothing if not bloody minded, painstakingly, painted the cobblestones. By the time he was done his suit, his one good suit, was ruined, covered in paint, but he couldn't care less. Next he threads the twine through the knockers of the doors on the street. Like lemmings he thought, we all got the same knockers. Made it easy to thread them all together.

All done, finally he tiptoes, and this for no reason other than enjoying the tiptoeing, anticipating the results of his mischief, across the street to climb up a lamppost.

Perched precariously on the cross bar, and with dawn creeping over the horizon, he fishes a half empty bottle from his pocket, takes a big pirate swig and tugs hard on the end of the twine. Timing is all, as the morning sun light illuminates his nights work.

Monkey swinging from the post as the doors knock, and the women of the houses, for it's them who are already up, it's them who come grumbling out of their houses to find Georgie Boy Pallen, the youngest of six boys and three girls to a local publican and wrestler, who always had to shout the loudest, grinning from ear to ear like the monkey he had been as a boy and still was, all covered in white paint.

'God fuck the king!' roars Georgie from the lamppost.

The same words now in huge capital letters on the cobblestones.

And the beating he got was fit for a king, husbands conjured from bed by the shrieks of their wives. Four of them, stumble out into the street, look up to see the culprit and the paint, and they surround the lamppost, swearing and shouting.

'Come down here Georgie you commie bastard, you bloody Yid, you fucking mug',

'You fucking lemmings, you ain't worth the shit off my shoes.'

Georgie spits back, as he kicks out with his foot at their grasping hands, huge dockers hands fishing for his foot, until they got him, pulled him down and beat him good and proper, until his wife beats them off, so as to get at him herself, lashing him with her tongue, her tears and her broomstick. The husbands skulked back indoors, but not before a round of, 'And fuck you 'an' all Georgie!'

Not least because he was right, not one of these men could give a fig for king, for country, for anything other than a quiet life and the pleasures of the pub, the whorehouse, and the track.

September 1938, Wally's office

Georgie Boy stood behind Wally's desk. He wouldn't sit down, but opened the drawer and gingerly took out the vodka. 'Shustov', the posh stuff, typical Wally. Georgie poured himself a few fat fingers and drank, then took out the gun, turned it over in his hand, felt its heft, sighted it, slid it into the back of his trousers like he'd seen them do at the flicks. He moved to the door but the gun dropped down the leg of his pants, so he had to take off his shoe to get at it, swearing, hopping, blood surging to his head as he bent down a bit pissed. Knackered now, Georgie wraps it up in the cloth, snatches the bullets from the drawer, and slams the door to his new office behind him.

Later, Lilliput Hall public house, Jamaica Road

The Lil, packed out, standing room only. Big men take up a lot of space. Stevedores, dockers, men used to wide arcs of space within which to work, handicapped by the cramped flats and busy pubs that cage them in their free time. The gaps filled in with narrow women, all hard work and disappointment. Georgie Boy sits with his brothers, their women, sisters and wives bringing them drink and food. He looks odd, demented, which is read by the room as grief. The book, Wally's book, its pages all stuffed back together, sits on the table in front of him. Pathetic looking, as if Wally's death had robbed it of something essential, not just the fact that it had been thrown from a first floor window into a puddle, its pages thrown to the wind. Georgie Boy meticulously smoothes out a page, a gesture of restoration, and reads from it. A big smile creases his face, a shock to some as up till now he has looked on the verge of tears. The book still retained the power of record.

Georgie Boy wonders what would have happened had he just burnt it.

'Last weekend's Police Boxing Championships. He'd take bets on anything'

Laughs, cheers, all round. He should have burnt it.

An old man shuffles into the pub unseen, only standing room right there by the door in the draught. And this man looks like he couldn't take many more of them, a lifetime of draughts, cramped doorways, etched into his face like so many IOU's.

'Jerry Collins had two quid on...'

And here he makes a show of reading a coppers name with both distaste and incredulity.

'Sergeant Peter Rowley, to win by knockout in the third round. Do we know, apart from Jerry here, the policeman's friend, if this was the case?'

Sniggers, shaking of heads until a voice cuts through.

'I was there, my brother's a copper.'

This from a thin man at the bar, with a big voice, holding a pint, a tattoo across his knuckles, which reads 'FAST'.

'I'm sorry for that, but did he win?'

'He did an' all, soon as they took away his stool, he was up and laid the fella out. Third round.'

His other hand comes up, involuntarily runs his fingers through his hair as all eyes rest on him, the word 'HOLD' now apparent across the run of his knuckles.

'Huh, sorry I missed it. That's good enough for me, Jerry. Here.'

Georgie marks off the bet, counts the money from a pile of coins and roll of cash in front of him, spilling from a sack like bag, its drawstring loosened. Jerry Collins steps up to collect his money.

The old man in the thinnest of suits which marks him out as a newcomer, a foreigner, makes it to the fire, the flames of which do not warm the reflection in his eyes. His profile almost that of a playing card, he stands.

'And finally, Doris, says here you had an each way on Brendan's cottage. Huh, backed that horse myself, not a large win but a safe one right my dear?'

'No such thing as a safe bet Mr. Pallen, you should know that.'

Her claw like hands scrape up the money, a few coins and they disappear between what's left of her breasts.

The thin man at the bar rubs his hands one over the other. A faded blue-grey swallow graces the back of his hand, its shape rippled by veins like a flag in the wind. 'This fist flies' is the meaning of that, or perhaps if we find any other swallows on this man, then distance travelled by sea, probably under sail, if we remind ourselves of the 'holdfast' across his knuckles. This ages him, although his face is timeless in the dim afternoon light of this Bermondsey saloon bar in September 1938. 5000 miles for each swallow. I wonder how many we would find. Sailors and coppers, it must run in families, same as publicans and bookies.

All settled then, Georgie slams the book shut.

'The rest is vigorish, for the family.'

He slides the money back into the bag and pulls the string tight. The audience turns back on itself, loses focus and becomes a crowd, a busy pub crowd out on the weekend. In the back room a woman sits with two small children. She has been weeping. The kids, well, they laugh and play and why not. Georgie places the bag of money and the book on the table. The woman, late 30s, not suited to tears, looks at the money, weighs it with her eyes.

'And then what, Georgie? When that runs out, what am I meant to do then?'

Georgie opens a silver cigarette case offers her one and lights them both. The time this takes allows for the return of some composure. They smoke, think.

'Marge is old enough to look after the little un' if I have to get a job.'

'I'll look after them babe, look after you. He said if anything should happen, he asked me to look after you.'

'You? Look after me? The fucking bookie's runner? Don't make me laugh. And don't call me babe neither!'

She smiles though, Georgie Boy too. Maybe there will be something between them, but not yet, not yet.

'Robin fucking Hood! Go on, urcha.'

Both of them are standing too close to each other for this exchange to be read at face value.

Outside the Lil' New Years Eve, 1939

Georgie cups his ciggy, bends towards the shorter man, Alf Rubin who lights him. Alf, aka 'Cayton', tipster for the *Daily Worker*, followed diligently by none other than the Queen herself that old soak and gambler, soon to be jeered and pelted with refuse on this very street.

Alf Rubin a small, sharp-on-his-toes Jew. Georgie spits, picking a loose strand of tobacco off his tongue. He's in fancy dress, a cowboy with hat, neckerchief, checked shirt and full leather chaps.

'Hitler, he's got it coming alright,' says Alf blowing out the match. They both smoke against the cold.

'That right King Bun? We've gone soft, since the general strike, mark my words, us lot up against the hun? This time round, who's your money on Alfie?

Cayton shrugs.

'You want my tip? Read the paper.'

Georgie passes him his hip flask, Alf takes a swig.

'The Russians, Alf? Is that what you want me to say? No mate, Stalin ain't daft, they'll sit it out. Watch us get fucked, wouldn't you? Same as the yanks. Sort Hitler out after he's knocked himself out.'

'I wouldn't be so sure.'

'What, you gonna give me odds? Don't make me laugh. Anyway, it's freezing. You coming in?'

'With you, dressed like that? Don't think so, I'm single Georgie.'

'Well then, happy hunting comrade.'

'Mazel Tov.'

Alf nods, walks down the street. Georgie tips up his wide-brimmed hat, bucks up his trousers, his chaps riding his hips like an oversized rubber ring and whips out his pistol, sighting it on Alf's retreating back, shoots and blows imaginary gun smoke from the barrel before wading in through the pubs swing doors, this bitter New Year that heralds nothing good for anyone.

Tower Bridge, December 8, 1940

Georgie on another bloody shout, this time close to home, the shelter at the arches next to that bloody bad luck pub, The John Bull. Why on earth did they build a shelter there? For some reason he was the first down the stairs, gagged, threw up in his own hanky from the smell. Cordite and cooked flesh and burnt vegetables from the poxy greengrocers next door, stank like some sick cannibal supper. Fuck me, fuck me, fuck me. Wally was right, the shit follows you, the stink, death, it knows you, sniffs you out, and it was sniffing here all right, pieces of bodies, like half a torso and whatever clothes it was in minced together, half man half fucking shirt, half kid half pram. He pulls on a pair of legs trapped under a block of cement. They come away without resistance, already severed from the rest, Georgie working by feel alone, his eyes so full of tears and smoke, his hands grabbing sinew and jagged bone.

Cut himself on a bloody bone he did, his small drop of blood adding to their gouts of it, a coppers whistle blowing for them to evacuate as the building was going to come down and he wanted then just to finish it, to be finished, to be crushed along with the rest, to have done. Bodies chopped in half, the rest, put better men than him in the nuthouse for life so why bother getting out? But in the middle of this, in all this, at the eye of this storm of feeling, flashes of thought and physical horror, Georgie hears a baby crying. A simple song that cuts through it all. His burnt and cut hands now wrapped in the clothes, the rags of the dead, he pushes over the body of a dead mother to reveal a baby gas mask, and a baby inside. He's not pulling on any baby legs not after what happened, but the whistle blows again, so he grabs the little diver, because that's what they look like in the gas mask, their little legs unprotected and open to the elements, easy prey for sharks is what Georgie thinks, what flashes through his mind as he closes his eyes and pulls.

Eyes tight shut, tears welling out like pus from a wound, for he can't afford to see it happen again, pulls and the baby keeps crying, legs still attached to the rest as the gas mask comes away from the ruined cave of its mother and Georgie screams, makes a sound for the first time in what feels like hours.

'Here! A baby! Alive!'

He stumbles out somehow, into the fresh air. He gasps, eyes still shut and feels the baby being taken from him, his arms light, his hands sore and wet with god knows what and he thinks, he thinks, Wally I ain't gonna be taken here, buried like this, slick with the blood of women and babies, in a shit ARP uniform. He opens his eyes, he never saw the baby, but it doesn't matter, Georgie Boy for once knows what he's going to do next.

Postscript:

The Lil New Year's Eve Fancy Dress Party, 1939

The old man, standing by the bar as far away as possible from draughts, but facing out into the pub, talking, to anybody who would listen, if they could understand Russian that is, now his tongue had been loosened by the brandy and his eyes, well they have taken on a glow.

His story, Moscow, 1916

We had a job that summer, human billboards marching up and down outside the Kremlin, embarrassing really but hey, it was money. Six of us like a walking card house, which was ironic seeing as that's where most of the money went. Straight down to the market in Khitrov, the Oreburka run card tables and bawdy houses, we couldn't help ourselves.

Advertising Shustov fucking vodka, another irony if that's the way you like to see things, Wally would drink himself silly on the stuff more nights than not. The whole deck of cards was about to come down, and I don't mind it if you think the metaphor is clumsy, because believe me I'm a simple man, and clumsy by habit, but walking up and down Red bloody Square as a billboard, well the humiliation at the very least was bound to cause an uproar if not a full-blown revolution in the heart and soul of a more modest man than myself. Wally, well he had ideas, when sober that is, ideas about how to set things right, and how to make the money to do it.

Georgie Boy bursts into the pub, waving his pistol, rooting tooting, roaring with the booze and the blood up, inhabiting the costume, the wild west energy coursing through his veins calling for the crack of gunfire and the smell of gunpowder, the sweat pouring into his eyes as he draws and fires above the bar, stumbles and fires again on his way down, catching the old man mid story in the thigh and the whole place now hushed and Georgie Boy coming down as quick as he went up, as he gets up, sobers up, 'Oh shit! Sorry, fuck me, get a doctor! Somebody get a bloody doctor!' applying the tourniquet himself using the bloody paisley neckerchief that came with the costume. The old man himself laughing at something else, an unknown irony perhaps, thank God he's drunk thinks Georgie Boy, that old man who knew Wally, sitting by himself, a face in the pub these last few years along with all the other incomers, the place overflowing, pouring what little money they had into Georgie's dads pockets, this his family pub, him his dads headache ever since he was knee high to a Chinaman. His dad a professional wrestler who could spill you across the room with one hand whilst pouring a pint with the other without spilling a drop.

George Pallen, publican, now older, unable to control his sixth son, his youngest, his namesake.

'George, Georgie Boy, when will all this palaver come to an end?' was about all he could manage, as the local quack dressed as Abraham Lincoln opened his work bag and began dressing the old mans wound, after he had been laid out on the saloon bar by Georgie, now to be seen holding him down, the old man spluttering what remained of his story into his ear.

PAUL REANEY
Standards Rule OK

Standing on the bonnet of a car. Like The Clash did.
On a Volvo. Down the posh street. Where the
doctors reside. And where the teachers live.
Smoking fags like a military general smokes his
victory cigar. Like The Clash did. Down the posh
street. Standing on the bandstand on the park. Like
The Jam did. Where the kids play. Where the dogs
bark. Breaking bottles, throwing stones. Setting
fires. Drinking lager like the dads in the pub do. On
the bandstand, like the Jam did, down the park.
Standing on the roof of Tesco. Like you're the
Pistols. Where your mum shops. Where your gran
buys her pepper and crisps. Battering the air
conditioners with metal bars. On the roof of Tesco.
Where your mum shops. Where your gran buys her
pepper and crisps.

And, oi, oi, oi, oi

And, when you are young

And, guns, guns, guns, guns on the roof

But just who is it you really are?

With your standards

As your career takes you off on a swerve

Standing on the drive outside your house. Like your
dad did. In the morning. Down your street. Where

your neighbours reside. And where your friends live. Needing a fag like a defeated union leader. Like your dad did. Down his street. Standing outside your garage. Where your kids play. Where your dog barks. Broken bottles, loose house bricks. Lager cans. Drunk just like you did. On the bandstand, when the Jam did, down the park. Your wife gets ready for work. The Tesco Metro. It's a Monday. After the weekend. You are off to work. You sell central heating systems. Fully fitted. Guaranteed. You have an issue. Your car's been done over. By kids. You didn't hear it. You were sleeping in the back bedroom. Your insurance will shoot through the roof. You know this.

On your drive. Stood with your kids. Your dog barking for you at your street

And the dinner party address

And the new rich red, a claret, it should be Beaujolais

And matching cutlery, M&S, Waitrose finest

Turn that racket down, I said

Young ones have got no respect

Listen, I'm going out, going out, going out, going out

Standing in the corridor of the hospital. Like you did. Your dad did. Trouble down your street. Where your neighbours reside. And where your friends live. Ambulances down your street. Unlike anyone in your family. Down their street. Standing on the bandstand on the park. Amphetamines. Booze. Cocktail. Your son did. Where the kids play. Where the dogs bark. Broken bottles. Loose stones. No fire except in the nostrils. Snorting powder like his mates did. On the bandstand, down the park. Leant on the bonnet of the car outside the hospital. Smoking fags like you're a no good.

Your regret is all this. The hurt your own heat-stop rush. Feel it. Your wife is inside with your eldest. Stomach pumped. Life can never be the same. You know this

You gather your other kids in the car

DEAN LILLEYMAN
Seventeen

or twenty I stepped into the window display of an
army surplus shop took a Luftwaffe jacket from a
dummy's back running twat-daft and drunk
through town chased by a man with one hand but
not very far because he had a gammy leg and that
night I went to the miners' welfare full of strut and
fuckery my new/old jacket that grey eagle carrying
its swastika too easily catching eyes eyes eyes as I
order barley wine the barmaid (forties) the
landlady (fifties) the old man at the bar (seventies)
tutting looking then tutting again as the landlady
says *not while you're wearing that* nodding at the
grey eagle arms crossed lips sucked in and the old
man says *disgusting* as the barmaid walks off
leaving me drinkless and to be fair I'd been at it all
day so to cut a long story short I got shouty didn't
get served went back home via the offy (the end)
but it's not because of one week later maybe three
a magazine in the dentist's waiting room had a
photo of a massive pile of dirty shoes so big it
would've taken ten minutes to walk round it and
on the next page a massive pile of skinny awful
bodies tangled up in a massive hole so bad I
couldn't look so that night I burned my new/old
jacket on the front-room fire but the next morning
it'd not all burned and that grey eagle was still
there so god knows what the binmen thought

MARTIN HAYES
Green-eyed Monster

In the twilight, Arthur thinks: *Any person who would try to come between a husband and his wife must really be evil in their heart. To do that, to look at a happy marriage and say to yourself 'I'm going to fucking wreck that, I'm going to mangle that just because I can.' That's just plain evil, right? That's one of the worst things a person could ever do.*

Arthur stands by the sink in his tiny kitchen, a bare bulb hangs from the centre of the damp-stained ceiling but it gives no light – a dead glass apple hanging from a three-core branch. You could feed it, but it will never grow. Arthur likes to stand and watch the coming darkness as it washes in across the bitter, leaning row of tiny houses which butt up against his concrete back garden. A playground for the lichen. A pitted grey nation, the rebar showing through like bones beneath H-Block skin. Rat-motorways through breeze-block tunnels and beer can tollbooths, their roofs caved in.

Arthur smiles that little smile of his; above the houses, the stars are coming out. The draining board is covered in pots and plates and cups. Things from dinner and breakfast. He has washed them but they do not look very clean. This room, like the others in the small terraced house, is rundown, in bad need of a visit from one of those television makeover shows. It smells of vinegar, even though no-one in the house cares for vinegar. It just always has. Ever since they moved in. Sometimes he wishes that they'd never come here. For it was better before. It just was.

Arthur knows that they're up to something.

He knows because of the fist that clenches deep in the pit of his stomach whenever he sees them together; laughing, caressing, sometimes even holding hands. At times the audaciousness of their betrayal overwhelms him, he becomes dizzy and lightheaded, he feels like he is falling from cliff. When the pain of this miasma engulfs him he has to squat down on his haunches and put his head between his knees. Sometimes the vertigo passes in seconds, sometimes it takes much longer.

They think that they're too clever for Arthur, but he knows all about them. He knows that Sarah's love for him has diminished since it all started five months ago. He can see it in her face. That pretty face which he is hostage to even when his eyes are closed. He also knows that it would not have been Sarah who instigated it. No, that job would have fallen to Michael. That cunt Michael who's supposed to be Arthur's friend, his pal, someone he can trust and depend on when the going gets tough.

In the darkness, Arthur bites his lip and wonders where it all went wrong.

How could he do it to me? How could they *do it?* Tears of hurt and shame run down Arthur's cheeks. He wipes them away with a damp tea-towel. He will not let the fuckers see his pain. He would rather die than let them know how much they've hurt him.

He can hear them even over the noise of the boiling kettle. He can hear them laughing and giggling in the front room. *For fucksake. They know I'm out here, they know I'm just feet away and still they carry on?*

That's what hurts Arthur the most. Not the fact that his wife's attentions have fallen on someone new, not the fact that he can see it in their eyes when they look at each other, not even the fact that more than once he has come home early from work and caught them in bed together (they tried to just laugh it off, like it was all a big joke). No, what really hurts Arthur, is the way they do it all right under his nose.

They don't even try to hide it. It's like he doesn't even exist. Like he's just some silly, inconsequential, impotent fuck-faced cunt.

And that might even be true, but still, there is one thing that Arthur knows as a solid fact. He knows that Michael will get his fucking comeuppance. He knows it because he's the one who is going to fucking give it to him.

Arthur's hands tremble as he reaches into the cupboard beneath the sink. His fingers settle on the brown glass bottle, which he has liberated from a store room in the hospital where he works as a porter. What type of poison the bottle holds, he is not sure, he knows only that he is thrilled in some way by the sight of the black skull and cross bones on the neon yellow label, and the phrase DO NOT SWALLOW – POISON written in big black bold bastard capitals beneath it.

He unscrews the cap, and looks down into the dark brown liquid. He looks and he thinks and for a split second, for a single fleeting moment in time, he almost doesn't go through with it. But then another wave of laughter carries down the hallway and makes the bile and spite rise in his throat. He tilts the bottle and the liquid begins to flow.

Arthur watches, transfixed, as it settles, slow and thick, reluctant to merge or emulsify with its host. *Oh, this is going to be good,* he thinks, *the look on that fucker's face when it hits the back of his throat! As it works its way down into his stomach! Burning! Polluting his organs!*

And is there a jury in the land that would convict him?

The bond between a husband and wife, that's something pure, yeah? That's still sacred, right? That's still . . .

But his train of thought is interrupted as Sarah walks into the room holding Michael in her arms. She flicks on the light-switch and says in that infuriating mock-childish voice, 'Daddy is a Silly Billy, isn't he, always standing around in the dark by himself.' Michael giggles and Sarah asks, 'Is his bottle ready?'

'Yes love, just about,' Arthur says shaking the bottle, watching as the brown poison slowly disappears into the foamy white formula.

'Here,' Arthur says, 'you can take your bath now. I'll feed him.'

Any person who would try to come between a husband and his wife must really be evil in their heart.

The more he thinks about it, the more Arthur knows this to be true.

ANETTE ROLLER
Handsome Devil

The past months had gifted their unsolicited shadows into her face and shattered any brightness and sparkling out of her eyes, which were once blue.

As she stood naked in front of the mirror to clean the large wound, holding her belly to fill the gap with hydrofiber, then applying the big hydrocolloid dressing, she tried to refuse looking at this abstract, terrifying cave.

She had her routine. She could've done it blindly.

It was four months ago since they had butchered the child out of her to save her precious, little life.

However, it had nearly cost her, her own life.

The last thing she remembered was Alex sitting well styled and perfumed by her bed when she woke from the anaesthesia, telling her with one breath that the baby was ventilated but beautiful and that he cannot take the responsibility and hereby ends their relationship.

No…affair.

Suddenly it was an affair.

The golden promises and plans, the true love he had left his wife for, exploded behind pink glasses like a bloated cadaver in the afternoon sun.

And it was in the afternoon, that two nurses lifted her out of bed to the sound of various beeping machine-protests and put her in a wheelchair. Surrounded by tubes and cables, with the urinary bag visible, they brought her to see the baby for the first time.

Five minutes!

Fuck you.

There she was, in nappies and a tiny wooly hat in rainbow colours, a life-supported, wee bundle, heaven-sent, in an incubator.

Her eyes wide open.

Belladonnablue wonders.

Instant conversation…eye-talk, gentle morsing via this invisible chord of souls.

Love beyond any love.

Love.

Breathtaking, beautiful little ivory child.

Let's make a pact, you and I. Us against the world and even the universe, if necessary.

After the Sepsis, the coma and the disbelief that Alex could leave her and his 'planned' child, his wife came to see her in hospital.

'I am here to warn you.'

He had never left her.

However, now she had filed the divorce.

'We were all fooled by him,' she said.

We were all?

We were all his number one.

She was lovely and weary, about 11 years older and the kind of woman men like to marry.

When she left, it was clear that he wasn't just an arsehole.

He was ill.

Bipolar.

That indeed now explained a few things during their short relationship. Affair. However, now he had stopped taking his pills.

Maniac.

After the fight for benefits, the cynical learning of the term – 'Maîtresse en titre' – and the wound still a 12cm open, oozing thing, Alex called.

He apologised with the pink glasses nicely wrapped up for her and she was in love but disgusted but a mother.

The handsome devil is a king of promises.

And this little girl at least should have the chance to be with her dad. Who was as charming as ever.

Now that his four other lifetime-loves weren't available for him anymore, she still believed in him. Too weak to resist and too far away from giving up.

Maniac?

He had shown an exquisite taste in his choice of pink glasses for her and appeared with a Ray-Ban himself.

And he blew her away with his handsomeness and elegance and surface perfectness.

He was too impressive.

She was a neuter with a newborn and her female body having failed at all levels.

Not able to have a safe pregnancy, not able to give birth, not able to breast-feed not able to keep the man who made all this happen in the first place.

Once again in her life, she felt like a useless, unworthy piece of crap.

So here comes the radiant, tall and attractive knight in very shining armour accidentally being her daughter's father and she shall refuse the chance to gain....dignity? And love?

Mindlessly, she asked herself, if mania is infectious and thus could open the door amused and smiling.

He entered her apartment like an invader.

Through the door without being asked to come in and looking around as if he was checking her case.

No asking for his daughter.

She was asleep in the bedroom.

He sat down on the couch, stretching out like a king, slowly taking off his sunglasses, smiling dentally correctly at her.

'I knew you would let me in and take me back,' he declared, his eyes fixed on a point far away somewhere outside the window. 'It's better for us both, you see. You haven't been fucked for a while and I have the money for you and your kid.'

She stood between couch and commode, holding on to the wall and listened to him releasing verbal diarrhea she hadn't expected.

'I'm getting divorced, by the way. Thank you for that. And do you remember? I had told you to have an abortion.'

He got up and walked around.

Now she noticed the sweat on his neck, parting his hairline in separate wet wisps.

'You became so imperfect, Alex,' she stated.

He shrugged in a tiny fit of control-freakishness and rapidly turned around to her.

She felt, as if she really should bring him to the door now. She was sick.

As if he had read her mind, he grabbed her by the wrists and pushed her to the white cold of the wall, her head colliding with it.

'I can show you perfection,' he said, releasing her hands, pressing her weary body to the wall and grabbing her breasts.

Too big for your hands, she thought and shoved him aside. Once more he reached out for her, this time grasping her crotch.

'I can smell your blood, you fucking whore.'

'Me?' she yelled at him.

'Don't judge me by your own shitty standards.'

Something inside her raged, wanting to puke her disgust onto his evening-sky-red Ralph Lauren shirt.

She was able to twist herself free from him and made her way through the corridor to the front door.

Just before she could reach it, he got a hold of her and pulled her close. His legs were so much longer than hers.

He turned her around with one hard move, grabbed her by her long blond curls and pushed her over the cabinet.

Cutting hair and dyeing it blood-red, she thought into her bucket list while he powerfully held her head down and kept her legs apart with his feet.

He began undoing his trousers and fumbling with her dress. She tried to reach him with her hands, but couldn't get any hold of him.

Strangely, she thought that screaming might not be a good idea because of the baby. Her little girl was asleep...she'd only wake her up and then she might be scared.

Somehow he had managed to pull up her dress and to drag her pants aside, and when he pushed his crotch angrily onto her arse, she could feel that he wasn't hard at all.

She felt relief; and it was the bottom drawer of the cabinet she hung over, that crashed into her mind. In there she kept her toys. The silicon dildo is harder than your bloody cock, she thought. He became more aggressive over his limp appendage than over her now.

Breathe in, turn around.

With her knee she kicked him to the wall behind him.

'Fucking leave!' she screamed and was quicker at the door than he was.

She opened it and stepped outside, screaming into the echoing staircase.

Alex was breathing hard, he seemed to evaporate like smoke from a candle.

She walked back in, grabbed him by the arm and pulled him outside.

'Never come back,' she told him and slammed the door shut.

Now the baby was awake with a sweetly gabbling voice. She went into the bedroom and looked into the bassinet. They smiled at each other.

'Daddy's gone now,' she whispered to her.

Then she took her out of her little nest and carried her, singing through the apartment.

FORD DAGENHAM
They Moved

downriver to thin terraces
with corridor rooms
and to estuary refineries
with banshee sirens
and chalk pits
of abandoned overgrown model T's
where they sat out air raids
singing in factory cellars
and Polish pilots smashed holed Hurricanes
into soft salt marsh
and tired horses delivered milk up the back lane
to the twin mad houses
where shell shocked Dunkirk soldiers
hid in Marks and Spencer doorways
from imagined
Axis spies
and grey cement car-parks
went up in prefab slabs
and lorries came
their children drove
and widened all the roads
and cheap concrete flowed down the river
covering old Victoriana
and
still they talk of the fish shops
and
the broken bells
cracked
ring

JOSEPH RIDGWELL
7/7

I was on a platform with a bunch of other commuters. The same faces, same frustrated silence, same dull routine. Then I was in a carriage, travelling via one of those silver tubes that regularly negotiate the world's largest underground public transport network. It was hot and stuffy on the Vicky Line. I was hungover.

At Highbury & Islington the driver made an announcement:

'King's Cross station is closed due to a power surge.'

That was my stop and Euston, the next stop, entailed a longer walk to the office. Irritated, my initial thoughts focused on the strong possibility of another suicide - there were two or three of those on the underground every week – but at Euston the train shuddered to a halt and we were told to exit the carriages. The train was going nowhere.

A further announcement on the public address system disseminated some vague information about the delay. There had been a huge power surge, or several power surges, and the entire London Underground network had been shut down. We were told to evacuate the station and seek alternative transport.

I shuffled amongst the disgruntled multitude towards the nearest exit, but we didn't get far. Access to the first set of escalators was blocked by hundreds of commuters.

A strange tension hung in the air and bad vibrations permeated the scene. It began hotting up and people, encouraged by the rising temperatures, started to shed apparel – jackets, coats and jumpers. The message to evacuate the station repeated itself, the disembodied robot voice sounding unsettling.

After the fourth or fifth repetition, a ripple of laughter emerged from the throats of the static crowd, but it was a

132

nervous laughter, a collective anxiety. How the hell were we meant to evacuate the station when nobody could move? At this rate of movement, or non-movement, we might be stuck underground for hours. Behind me a man collapsed against a wall, breathing heavily, fumbling for an inhaler. Nobody asked if he was alright or if he needed any help, everyone concentrating on getting out, somehow.

It was each to their own.

Gradually the air became thin, almost suffocating, and a panic hit me. What if this was a chemical or terrorist attack? It had long been a threat, and the general consensus amongst your average Londoner was that it was only a matter of time. Maybe this was that time. I looked left and right, eyes peeled for an alternative exit, a speedier way out of this going nowhere scene.

Then a man showed in the crowd, a lone wolf, walking in the opposite direction to everybody else. Acting on instinct I followed him, weaving around static bodies, until I was right behind him. Nobody else came with us, but then we *were* walking away from the exit. It didn't matter; if there was no other exit then we would return and re-join the non-moving crowd.

Further down the platform four women were arguing with two underground staff, one becoming hysterical. She was screaming and shouting, she couldn't breathe, was going to die unless they got her out of the station. The harassed guards threatened to call the police. Behind the guards was an emergency exit. The stranger and I saw it. Without saying anything, and with the guards pre-occupied with the hysterical woman, we headed towards the exit.

We slipped inside the door and turned into a narrow winding staircase rising upwards. We jumped the stairs two by two saying nothing. My only thought was to get out of the station as quickly as possible because I didn't want to die. Was I overreacting, freaking out? Probably, but I didn't care, I just wanted to get the fuck out of that hole.

Up and up and up, higher and higher, and with every step the fear receded. At the top of the staircase a closed door confronted us. The man reached out a hand and the door opened. The stranger and I exchanged nervous smiles, the last time we made any connection.

Outside, I breathed a tremendous sigh of relief. The underground must be the worst place on earth to be trapped in, entombed in the bowels of the earth. Out on the streets my first thought was to get to the office, find out what had happened. There were hundreds of people everywhere, disorientated, frantic, dazed. Police sirens filled the air and Old Bill were everywhere. There were fire engines, ambulances, even a couple of helicopters. What the fuck?

I crossed an empty Euston Road, usually blocked with traffic during the mornings rush-hour, and made my way to Tavistock Place. I passed a man covered in soot, he must work in a dirty place, I thought. But he was wearing a shirt and tie. Weird. I turned a corner and an almighty bang, like a million air-bombs had been let-off simultaneously, ripped through the surrounding area, throwing me to the ground. I lay on the pavement dazed, ears ringing. What the fuck was that?

People ran past, someone trod on my leg, it hurt; a good sign.

Then I checked myself, nothing missing, hands, arms, legs, feet still there, not even a cut, and no blood. I looked up, clouds of black smoke rose skywards and papers fluttered around. I stood up warily, and stuck my head around the corner to see what had caused the explosion.

And there it was.

A London bus I'd passed moments earlier was now a wreck, the roof peeled away like an opened lid on a tin of sardines, glass and debris everywhere. Some people on the exposed top deck, unmoving, static. An old man hanging from the bottom deck, dead, a torso in the road, a wall splattered with blood, flesh, and gore. More sirens and then an unnatural, deathly silence, punctuated by terrible screams; from the wounded and the dying, and the damned.

Only one thought now, get the fuck out of there.

I found a small park and sat down on a bench and tried to regain my composure. Then my thoughts turned to others, anyone who might have used London's public transport system that morning. Several doomsday scenarios ran through my mind's eye, each one more terrible than the previous.

Then my mobile rung.

It was my sister.

'There's been a bomb on the Underground.'

'And on a bus, I just saw it, no roof, dead people.'

My sister fell silent, like something had distracted her attention.

'Come home. It's terrible, there are more bombs.'

'Are you watching the news?'

'Yes, there are more bombs, several bombs. How will you get home?'

'I'll walk, cut through Islington and Hackney. Can you tell Mum I'm okay?'

'Yes, yes, come home, you promise?'

'I promise, don't worry. I'll ring you when I get to Leyton.'

'Okay.'

I began walking away from Kings Cross and Euston, and Tavistock Place where the bus was, its roof ripped away. Gruesome images of the old man flashed through my brain, his dead body, hanging there like a rag doll. Then I thought about the limbless torso. Who was responsible? I didn't know, didn't care. I just wanted to go home.

A taxi appeared, light on, I stuck out my arm and it pulled over.

'Where to mate?'

'Walthamstow.'

'Can only take you as far as Whitechapel.'

'Why?'

'Gotta stay close to the city, gonna be a busy day, what with all the bombs going off.'

I was stunned into silence. Innocent people had just been blown to pieces and this mercenary cunt was more concerned with how much money he could earn out of the situation.

I waved the rapacious cabbie away and continued walking. Had I cheated death? Maybe, maybe not, but the experience had me freaked. Who was responsible? Who would do such a thing? Life was short, today alive, tomorrow dead, blown up trying to get to work. I didn't even like my job. What a crazy fucked up world we lived in, an age of terror, a crap age. There was no glory in terror, no romance, no heroism, nothing but pointless carnage.

Then something remarkable happened. The city stopped working.

Suits emerged from buildings all over the Square Mile, first just a few hundred, but eventually thousands of city workers left their places of employment at exactly the same time.

I joined an army of Suits heading east.

We marched the streets of London in silence.

We were all going home.

JENNI DOHERTY

Almost There

A cluster of girls gathered on the dance floor in front of
him. Tall, fat, short, thin shapes; dancing,
butts out, moving in circular motion,
galvanic orange-tinged limbs swaying without
inhibition, unchained and free as they would never be in
daylight.
The fierceness of their glares matched by that of their
joy; yellow-to-white teeth bared.
Flashing laser lights picking up the dust and curdling
smoke, reflecting rings in ears, noses and lips.
All James could do was stare in amazement.
Outnumbered, he made his way
to the bar and ordered a double.
Being single wasn't easy, he thought.

No Rehearsal

Her face sears, a mask of hot prickles, when people
stare. Unseeing strangers. The quiet makes her shiver.
She has a sense of herself, twinkling,
in that cluster of hushed seconds. Silver screen swells
with colour, pulses, hurls light. Upturned faces licked by
ghostly beams. Whispers simmer with back-seat parties
as secret sensations rise.
There he is: a creature struck stupid by torch-wink. An
awesome eye, face whacked angelic with light.
Above the shimmer of lips, her eyes sting, stunned.
Can he see her?
Everyone folds back into velvet; squirming laughter,
creasing faces, oblivious.
First date – no rehearsal

RAYMOND GORMAN
INTERVIEW

Derry born and bred, Raymond Gorman is best known
as the guitarist/songwriter with That Petrol Emotion,
who he co-founded with John O'Neill out of The
Undertones. Often hailed in the music press as a band
before its time, they were attributed as one of the first
pioneers of independent bands to fuse both funk and
dance into what was often a very hard hitting guitar
and lyrical sound. The band released five very
successful studio albums that included *Manic Pop
Thrill* and *Babble* and had underground hit singles with
It's A Good Thing and *Big Decision*. Four of the
members of the same band have formed a new band,
The Everlasting Yeah. Raymond has also written
poetry, features and fiction regularly for PUSH and he
was in the much sought after Issue One. He met with
Joe England south of the River Thames for food and
drinks at The Marmaris restaurant in Balham.

JE: For starters, Irish writers. Who is your favourite?
RG: Well, I'd probably say it has to be Flann O'Brien,
because he's got a brilliant sense of humour and I really
connected with him. We did one of his books at school, *The
Poor Mouth*, which we studied in Irish as *An Béal Bocht*, and
it's such a fantastic book. In fact if you read it in English
you're not going to get everything, because there's a lot of
Gaelic puns in it, Irish language puns, there's a lot of taking
the micky out of Irish history and in particular it's a parody
of the poor, downtrodden, unfortunate Paddy; always under
the thumb of the English and living under the eternal
downpour. O'Brien reduced that classic Irish archetype to its
most absurd kind of form. There's a character called Sitric
O'Sanasa who lives on a rock, has absolutely no possessions,
lives off fish by diving into the sea to catch them, and is
famed throughout Ireland for the excellence of his poverty. I
just loved it. There are so many jokes in it and when we were
studying the book we'd sit there in stitches. And then I found
out more about him, read his letters and a couple of his other

books, but I couldn't get into *The Third Policemen* which I know everybody loves.

JE: I'm one of those who love it. The ending is one of the creepiest you'll ever read. You need to give it another go, trust me.

RG: I'll give it another go. But some of his short stories and his articles in the newspapers really used to make me laugh. He used to have this thing about bores, people who bored you to death in the pub, like this guy trying to tell you how many shaves he could get out of a razor, that was the kind of conversations, completely absurd, but I loved it.

JE: There's a story about *The Third Policemen* and how it got rejected countless times, and the final time he told friends when on the train on the way home, how the whole manuscript flew out the window and it was found hidden in his house caked in layers of dust just after he died, and I think this adds to its brilliance, perfection, not for him obviously, as he didn't get any kind of acknowledgement for the book when he was alive, but it goes to show how often publishers get it wrong. But if you're someone that indulges in drugs and drink and have an imagination, and know a good book, well, it's *The Third Policemen* all day long.

RG: The thing is, he was a heavy drinker. He comes from Strabane, County Tyrone, that's where my mum comes from. And there's footage of him on YouTube with Brendan Behan and Patrick Kavanagh on Bloomsday and they are all so plastered. Those guys would have been in the pub from morning to night.

JE: Brendan Behan was the first Irish writer I read. *Borstal Boy*. Just the opening part where he is arrested in Liverpool blew me away. It's an honest book, brilliantly written, and you get that this is a sixteen year old in Borstal, an Irish terrorist, who has a definite connection with people, working class people, and that at sixteen he was very well read.

RG: They are actually an amazing family the Behan family. There was a great book about the mother called, *The Mother of the Behans* by Brian Behan. I met him some years ago when I lived in the Borough. There was an Irish week on in Southwark that was just fantastic. They showed *The Dead*, John Huston's last film based on the classic Joyce short story, and Brian Behan himself was there talking about his mum and the family. He's a trade union guy as well, salt of the earth, and of course there's the other brother Dominic who wrote *The Patriot Game*. They were an interesting and talented family.

JE: I read in Bendan Behan's biography by Ulick O'Connor how he fell out with Dominic the instant he heard his brother was writing too and he famously said, 'The cat at number ten will be writing next!'

RG: Brendan was a great writer for sure. As I said though, they were all talented. We had a great quote from Behan on one of the That Petrol Emotion albums: 'civility costs nothing'. I try to live by that myself.

JE: Now I made contact with you through Liam Tyrell, and we both used to write for the same West Ham fanzine and he said I should get in touch with you. And I did.

RG: Whenever it was you contacted me, I felt instantly good about it, I didn't know you from Adam but I just had a feeling that something good was going to come out of this, something substantial.

JE: And it has. I think for me, you have been involved with PUSH from day one and you have been featured in nearly all the issues. But what you did, that I think was so important in those early days, was put it out there to a larger audience and through that I became very connected with writers who became strong components of the mag ever since. Two in particular are Ian Cusack and Anette Roller. But also others. And I have got to thank you for that. People say I have done really well and all that, but I rely on passionate contributors and you have always been supportive and I was wondering, what was the very first thing you wrote as it is a question that always intrigues me.

RG: My brother says I was writing all the time but I don't really remember much of it. The first one or two things that I ever wrote that I thought were any good, was some poems for a school magazine when I was ten. That was the last year of primary school. Two poems got published in the school magazine. I was in a quite exceptional class. I think there were 32 of us, and all 32 passed their eleven plus. And there was some real brain boxes in there. No way did I think I was ever in the top tier, but it was only years later I realised how good some of my stuff was. Again my brother, he always says to me, 'you peaked at ten!' But priests had the ability of knocking the confidence out of you, so I really never thought I was any good. I had low self esteem, same as a lot of working class kids at that time, but it was kind of good having an education, though I did kind of drift through. I wanted to be a footballer but after sixteen I started drinking and smoking and I just didn't have the discipline anymore. I was actually quite good at football. I love football.

JE: I'm still really fascinated by that period you are talking about. What was that first moment when you looked around and realised things were not quite what they seemed?

RG: I think it was 1968. We moved house that year, same year the Civil Rights all kicked off, and we moved from a two bed house overlooking the Catholic Bogside to a three bed in an area a bit further out, where there was still a lot of Protestants living. I went to a Catholic boy's school but outside of that, I used to hang around with the Protestant kids on my street, so it was mixed and a great experience though not without danger. Eventually the Protestants would all move over the river to the Waterside, which made for more segregation, all very sad. So the first seven years of my life were really very happy and then The Troubles happened. The first big thing for me was when my dad and my uncle took me on the Civil Rights march and we got chased by the police with water canons, so that was incredibly exciting, for a seven year old. But I remember my dad saying to me, he was kind of shaken, saying, 'You'll always remember this, this is history in the making.' So to be in the centre of all that has had a big impact. My whole life has been Civil Rights. If people ask me what's my politics? Civil Rights.

JE: I told you about my first time in Derry and seeing kids who were younger than me stoning the army vehicles, PIGS they were called, and I was a small boy but they were even smaller, and it was a wake up call to real life. Because I had no idea before I got there what The Troubles were really all about. Everyone was really friendly though, but there was always this sinister undercurrent that something really bad could happen at any minute.

RG: You see when you came out there that wasn't too long after Bloody Sunday had happened. And anyone will tell you Derry has never been the same since Bloody Sunday. And there's something still hanging in the air. I can still feel it when I go over there. It's a negative energy that seems to envelope the whole place, holding things back. But saying that, every time I do go back these days, I enjoy it more and more.

JE: Before we talk about your current band and previous bands, what are your brief recollections of The Undertones?

RG: At the start I couldn't get in to see them. Because they played at this place called The Casbah, which was basically a glorified portakabin, so the thing is I couldn't get in cos I looked too young but my other mates could, so some of us used to stand outside and you could hear just as good from there. Actually I think the sound was better from *outside*. You had a bit of a buffer zone. So that's when I first got to hear them live but I already knew Damian O'Neill who I had gone to school with, in fact I've known him since I was about four. Anyway, whenever they came back from tour, there's this thing in Derry where you're not allowed to talk about what you're doing if you're in any way successful, and of course they were quite big news, doing really well, but they'd get a lot of stick. They did a free gig one time in the Bogside, not long after *Teenage Kicks,* and they got pelted with eggs by some wee local hoods. Now can you explain to me the mentality of that? People were thinking that they had gotten too big for their boots, which was crazy as they were so down to earth. You could walk into any of the pubs in town and they'd be there and they'd talk to you. None of them had any airs or graces. The thing with Damian, he enjoyed travelling, same as me. I'd been all the way over to France and was by that time at University and he wanted to go live in London which was buzzing at the time with punk, but the others were tied to staying in Derry. They had their girlfriends there and didn't want to leave to go on tour much. He was the youngest in the band and he'd come over to London to do all these gigs and then he had to go back to Derry again. He was gigging and wanted to stay in London and enjoy himself, be proper rock and roll. So Damian eventually moved over and he could talk to me about all the things they were doing as he knew I wouldn't get all judgemental, and it was the same for me as well as I could tell him all the stuff that I was doing, all the travelling and hitchhiking I'd been doing around Europe.

JE: So was That Petrol Emotion formed in London then?

RG: No, it was formed in Derry. Me and John (O'Neill) formed the band. It's really funny actually, the last Undertones gig down in Southern Ireland was at this festival and me and my friend Mickey went down to see them. It was a two day festival and I met some other friends of mine on the second day there and they gave me some vodka and stuff. I stayed drinking with them and ended up passing out and missing the gig, I was actually passed out in their dressing room and they put me on the bus with them back to Derry that night, so I landed back in Derry about four in the morning and I couldn't go home of course as I was supposed to be at this festival and I'd missed the gig and had nowhere to stay and John said come and crash at my house. So that's how I got to meet him. So then my friend Mickey had to bring both our rucksacks back and he was really fucked off as you can imagine, but that was my introduction to John and we became friends and soon decided to do this club night, a disco, and we'd get together twice a week and decide what to play. In the meantime I'd go round the town and buy up all these records from the bargain bins, really cheap usually about 60p. I picked up some amazing records. It was a great club. We played a real cross section of everything, electro, early hip hop, classic soul, reggae, punk, you name it we played the best of everything. It was called The Left Bank Disco. Sixty to one hundred people came on a regular basis. And it was like a religion to those people. It was like the best crack. You talk to John and he'd agree with me that that was one of the best times ever. I still have nothing but great memories. So as we got friendly I'd start saying to him, don't you want to be writing songs again? At first he'd say no as he was pretty fed up with the way The Undertones ended but eventually without me saying anything he got inspired again by the records we were playing at the Left Bank week in week out. As I was naturally really enthusiastic and passionate also about music I think he realised he'd found a kindred spirit. I was also at the time in a great wee local band called Bam Bam and The Calling, my first band. So basically from always wanting to be in a band to not doing anything until I was 22, all of a sudden I was DJing and in two bands and it was like, fantastic, some of the best years of my life. John really liked Bam Bam too and I think he was sort of sizing me up for his next project and he said a couple of things to me, like whenever I listened to a record I would be drumming on my legs and he could see that my sense of rhythm wasn't bad and then he saw me play guitar and was impressed by the music and how I could tune okay by ear. At some stage he thought *this guy could be a goer*, and he started writing some stuff and invited me up to have a listen and I started writing with him as well which was great for my confidence. I wrote the words to *Blindspot* as a poem and he took it away and came up with the whole thing. By that time Ciaran (McLaughlin) had heard that we were starting to play and getting a band together and he sent a letter to John asking to join. And it's a really funny letter you know saying he's surviving on whisky, aspirin and Van Morrison records. It was really funny, made us laugh. But we knew he was a great drummer. He used to deputise for Billy (Doherty) as Billy kept leaving The Undertones and one time Ciaran played on a tour of France when he was only fifteen or sixteen. And you see the video of him playing and he's so comfortable he makes it look so effortless. The man is such a great drummer. So in October 1984 the three of us decided to move over to London to try our luck, picking up Damian who by that time was finally living there and within a year we'd picked up Steve Mack the Yank singer along the way.

JE: So the band finally comes together and then you put out *Manic Pop Thrill* which is one of your greatest albums. I've told you that. I've still got my original on orange vinyl. It's a brilliant album.

RG: I'm very proud of it.

JE: And it captures an essence of The Troubles. Was that intentional?

RG: It captured the frustration we felt I think about what was going on in Ireland. We steered away from sloganeering and all that kind of obvious stuff. We had a special time making that record.

JE: 'It's A Good Thing' was a classic pop song. Still sounds fresh.

RG: Well that has a lot to do with Hugh Jones the producer. That song was originally a big sprawling number, a bit like Television, with loads of guitar all over it, and basically Hugh Jones just came out and said, this is a pop song. So what he did was change it. He knew how to arrange it. He cut out this long middle bit with all the guitars, said it was too meandering, not really going anywhere, and we sort of stood back and went, yeah, yeah, you're right. So all of a sudden we had this brilliant pop song.

JE: It is one of your great moments. Talking of which. I could never understand why the album *End of Millennium Psychosis Blues* didn't get the recognition it deserved.

RG: There was a review in the NME where they gave it 8/10, but if you read the whole review it was like an obituary. And I thought, the knives are out here.

JE: Well to counter that, I loved it, and because of that album cover I began smoking Lucky Stripe cigarettes! Never heard of them before. You are partly accountable for a continued nicotine addiction. But I did think it was a great album. Played it to death when it came out. Anyway. Moving on. The intended theme for the next issue is drinking. So, you've now long crossed over to the other side, and as I have clearly demonstrated tonight, I haven't, but can you explain how and why you went from the rock and roll life to becoming clean and who you are now?

RG: Around the time of *End of the Millennium* when we were just about to go in and make this record, everyone was in great form and John turned round out of the blue and says he's leaving! So he just killed the whole fucking atmosphere before we had played a note. And even now I'm still thinking why did he do that at that time? Why not wait until the album is finished and then tell us. It created this terrible atmosphere. For years I couldn't listen to the album, it had really bad connotations for me. When we were recording, there was tension all the time. Because things just weren't spoken. Typical men. Keeping quiet, letting stuff build up. I was starting to get really out of control with drink and drugs anyway about then. It was really tense all the time, unbearable. John did one more tour with us before leaving so the bad times seemed interminable. I found myself in a very dark place. Used to do acid quite a lot but then had one bad trip. I had broken the cardinal rule. Don't do acid when you are not feeling too hot, and of course it triggered a whole series of depressing episodes, and I ended up in the Priory; not the Priory itself but a kind of an equivalent. It was full of all these rich junkies from Chelsea and I was sent there and all was paid for by Virgin. When I found out how much it cost I felt guilty. It was ridiculous, £200 a day or something. But these rich junkies were mostly a joke. They had no intention of getting clean in the long term, their daddy or mummy had put them in there, pretty much a holiday for them. But with me, I was in a real state, I really was. I was completely paranoid, didn't trust anybody, couldn't sleep. I'd been doing loads of speed, smoking dope and drinking heavily. I just kept going. And so I had gone about a week without getting any sleep, was very psychotic, and thankfully they put me in the hospital where I could rest and recover. I slept for about three days to start with. I don't know what they gave me, downers or whatever it was to help me sleep, but I did and when I woke up I immediately felt better. There was a bit of clarity and I thought, do you know what, I don't want to do this anymore. I didn't think I was rock bottom, but what used to happen with my drinking before then was I was partying quite a lot and when you're young you can get away with it. But I also was doing a lot of acid. And I was just swapping one thing for another. But after the hospital, I got better. Eventually. But it took a long time as I was still drinking, and a couple of times I ended up in the cells. I woke up at Holborn police station one time and got kicked out at 5am in the morning. I didn't even remember going in there. I'd been at some party up the Holloway Road, but I have no idea what happened. Walked home from the cells, took me about an hour, got in about 6am and saw I was covered in fucking cuts and bruises. But I think it was my falling rather than anyone hitting me, and it was all like, shit, I really don't remember anything at all. Nobody would speak to me. My sister and my best friend wouldn't speak to me, so there were issues and I wanted to stop but the band was still there and playing. Whenever I went away with the band you'd go into the dressing room and they'd be eighty cans of beer, five bottles of wine, two bottles of spirits, you know what I mean? And if you go to somewhere like Leicester on a Tuesday and there's nothing to do, you'll have a beer and start off a bit early. But a defining moment for me was when I woke up in the cells that time. I was messed up, I'd messed things up with women, good women, and ended up with others who I shouldn't have been with. All quite heavy drinkers like me. There was one woman who I was with for a while, and even though I didn't want any kind of commitment we'd go out, get drunk and end up together at the end of the night. I felt bad after that. I was just using her. But I definitely had a lot of self esteem issues going on.

JE: All of our lives are impacted with self esteem issues. How we function and engage with one another is all down to how we feel about ourselves. Well I think that was very honest of you to come out with that and the fact you are now clean is very honourable, says me as I finish this bottle of wine.

RG: Yeah, you haven't held back there!

JE: It helps me with my self esteem! Listen, you're in a new band.

RG: The Everlasting Yeah.

JE: And I saw you about a year ago at The Roundhouse, superb gig, brilliant night all round.

RG: It was a good night.

JE: The bar was like being transported to a bar in Derry. I think me and Michael Keenaghan were the only two with English accents! So anyway, who is in the band?

RG: Well, it's the four Irish members of the last line up of That Petrol Emotion: Damian, Brendan, Ciaran and myself. Which, with Steve Mack obviously, was actually my favourite line up of the band. When Brendan joined the band everything clicked and we moved up another couple of gears. Damian was never really a bass player. As good as he was, he was always a guitar player. But Brendan gives us that solid bottom end and backbone. Ciaran loves playing with him.

JE: As a unit you are definitely very strong. Great live, you really are. Now you have got this new album all finished. Tell us about it.

RG: *Anima Rising* is the name, and it's seven songs, forty eight minutes, and I think it is the best thing I have ever put my name to. In the past we always had a problem capturing the live energy and the kind of excitement that the live gigs had. But I think we've really nailed it here and there's that thing when we first went into the studio and we were just ready to explode. We knew we had good songs. We knew we were ready to go, And we met with the guy who recorded us, he was the drummer in Stereolab, a great guy, and there was a good atmosphere in the studio and everyone felt comfortable, and we banged it all out very quickly.

JE: How much input did he put into the album?

RG: Well I think he created the conditions for things to happen and to work fast. He's a good guy, he captured the sound, a great engineer, and he's a drummer, so he got everything sorted for Ciaran, which was really important. On previous occasions there's like a day or two just trying to get the right drum sound. In some cases even replacing Ciaran's drumming altogether! He's had three of our records where his drums were replaced by samples. That's crazy. Really horrible. But that was the 80s and nothing to do with now. We produced this album and spent quite of lot of time doing the production. And it was worthwhile. It sounds fantastic. I think there's three/four singles on the album. I do. I've been playing the album to everyone I can and they all love it. I'll play some to you in the car after. I've played it to some folk who are often too cynical for their own good and a journalist who I know quite well, who never really liked Steve Mack's vocals, and he heard the album and I swear he freaked out, loves it. As I said, it's the best thing I have put my name to.

RAYMOND GORMAN

Friends & Enemies

The restoration
of dharma
is in my blood

and the river of
my heart's dreams
has now become a flood

this ain't no time
for half-baked
solutions or remedies

for now
my corporeal friends
have become
my spiritual enemies

THE
EVERLASTING
YEAH

ANIMA
RISING

STEVE FINBOW
The Trail

If time travel is invented in my lifetime, there are a few
points in my history I'd like to revisit. Of course, I'd put
better use to it—nip back to the 1870s and have a few
pints with Verlaine and Rimbaud in The Parrs Head in
Camden Town—I'm dying of thirst, suffocating, I can't
cry out. It's eternal torment. Drop by Café Cyrano to
eavesdrop on the Surrealists. Or grab a booth in The
West End bar in the 1950s, and argue with Bill, Jack and
Allen. They know that the name of the game is survival.
But what I'd really like to do is go back to those times
when I feel like I could have done better, acted
differently, said the right thing, pulled out in time. It is a
dark disaster that brings the light.

I was 13, just getting into music, literature, art, drugs,
drink, and girls—an unlimited right of all-powerful
monstrosity. My local football club—Brentford FC—had
invited me for a trial. It is not necessary to accept
everything as true, one must only accept it as necessary. I
had to be at Feltham Arena at 8:30am. My grandfather
picked me up in his light-blue Ford Popular and drove
me there. We got there in plenty of time and I went into
the changing room to put on my kit. No-one would
perform the merest action without the feeling that this
action is the one and only reality. Most of the boys were
my age and most of the boys were taller and heavier. I
was skinny, short, had a mop of curly blond hair. The
other boys' hair seemed neat and short—professional.
The haircut, for example, half shorn, devoid of
affectation and above all of definite shape, is without
doubt trying to achieve a style completely outside the
bounds of art and even of technique, a sort of zero degree
of haircut. I put on the shirt they gave me and looked at

the board. I was in the starting eleven. That was good. I was playing inside left. That was good as well. We ran on to the pitch. The game was fast. The other boys were very good, better than I expected. The range of what we think and do is limited by what we fail to notice. And because we fail to notice that we fail to notice, there is little we can do to change; until we notice how failing to notice shapes our thoughts and deeds. I didn't touch the ball for the first five minutes.

Then it came to me along the ground. I controlled it on the move, my back to the defender, flicked it past him, moved on to it, looked up, no-one there from my team, took a half-decent shot. Goalie saved. Not bad, I thought. Walking back, I looked at the touchline—the man who gave us instructions at the start was shaking his head. What did he want me to fucking do with the ball? The only danger in this is that the virtual could be confused with the possible. Next few minutes, I was fouled a few times. I'd obviously rattled the defenders. Then the ball came to me, similar position as before, this time I went outside the defender and, as he turned, turned inside him, ball on my left foot, another defender came across, I nutmegged him but a bit too hard and, as I ran around him, the ball moved over to my right and bobbled a bit on the turf. I hit it with the outside of my right foot and it curled long and fast into the bottom right-hand corner of the net.

A combination of circumstances has marked almost everything I have done with a certain air of conspiracy. I wheeled around. Someone patted me on the shoulder. The other players walked back to the centre circle. A man shouted at the goalkeeper, 'Next time, get in the right bloody position.'

At half-time, someone told me I was coming off. I didn't understand. Maybe I'd done enough already. That was it. An immense indecipherable continent of hunger—certainty there could never again be a chance. After the game, we were told to shower and then the names of players who had been successful would be posted on the door. I washed and dressed and waited until the boys and their relatives were crowding around the list. The void frees me from what attaches me. In the void there is nowhere to stop.

As I stepped over to check my name was there, my grandfather came out of the group, put his arm around my shoulder, led me away. There is in the human breath sudden shifts and breaks of tone and, from one scream to another, abrupt transferences, and a sickening quietus.

MICHAEL KEENAGHAN
Friends

I sat parked up from the off licence trying to see through the belting rain. Sammy and Bigz were due to burst from the shop's doors any second, but they were taking their time, and if they didn't hurry up I'd be burning rubber without them. One last job, Sammy had said, telling me he had all the intel, the safe was loaded, a payout I'd be crazy to refuse. Six months ago I'd have needed no persuading, but I had priorities now. A steady girlfriend, a baby daughter, the first stable set up of my life. Sammy and Bigz had better not be fucking this up.

Then there they were, running along the street in their balaclavas – followed by four bat-wielding Asian guys. They jumped in shouting at me to Go! and I pulled out, the car under assault, one of them jumping onto the back, his face pressed to the glass as I sped along the street, the boys panicking until I swerved at the next corner and he was gone.

'What the fuck happened back there?' I shouted when we were back on the North Circular.

Sammy was next to me, pulling off his mask and running his hands over his cornrows, Bigz in the back, both of them out of breath.

'We got nothing,' Sammy said. 'It was like an ambush. Five, six guys jumping out from nowhere.' Then he took out his Glock handgun, staring at it. 'And I had to use this thing.'

'Tell me it was a warning shot, please.'

He shook his head and I slammed the wheel.

'Jesus!'

'Listen,' Bigz leaning forward. 'If Sammy hadn't shot the guy we'd have never got out of there. And anyway, the guy fucking deserved it. You should have heard him back there – he was shouting at his sons to kill us.'

'And what if the guy's dead? I don't believe this. You're useless, the both of you.'

Bigz kissed his teeth.

'Who are you calling useless, you fucking prick.'

'Shut it fatman, I'm not in the mood.'

'Yeah, you want to pull over and settle this then?'

The cussing continued until Sammy erupted.

'SHUT THE FUCK UP, THE PAIR OF YOU! Serious shit has happened tonight. We've got to be together on this.'

For the first time ever, Sammy looked nervous.

'We're in trouble,' he said. 'I think I shot him in the neck.'

'No way. It was the arm, the shoulder maybe. Minor shit.'

'I don't think so, B. The amount of blood, didn't you see it?'

Right then all I could see was prison. And no silly few months this time either. Thinking fast I took a turn, heading for Wembley.

'Where we going?'

'Somewhere I know. We're burning this thing. And Sammy, say goodbye to your Glock.'

We torched the car on some wasteland and buried the gun. Then we headed to my Uncle Roy's house. It was a big ask, but who else could I turn to?

Luckily he was welcoming.

He took our clothes and we cleaned ourselves of gun residue. Roy was an old lag himself, but taking me aside he told me he was disappointed in me.

'What happened Jase? I thought you were finally pulling yourself together?' Then he gave me some advice. 'If you get away with this – and you'll be lucky if you do – ditch the buddies. Get rid of them. Blokes like that will just drag you down.'

By the door, kitted out in whatever odds and ends he could find, we thanked him.

'Okay, now piss off, get out of here.'

We owed him one.

I woke up the next morning with Mel stroking my chest and saying she'd just got Kellie off to sleep. Her hair was down and she was wearing my favourite bra. But I wasn't in the mood. I jumped up and headed to the living room, firing up the laptop to scour the London news.

A Cricklewood shopkeeper is today recovering in hospital after being shot in an attempted robbery.

I read on. But the guy was alive, making a recovery and that's all I wanted to hear.

Then I looked up and saw Mel in front of me, in tears.

'You don't love me anymore. It's since I had Kellie, isn't it? I'm twice the size and you don't want me.'

I stood up, clicking into gear.

'No way. I've just had a lot on lately, that's all.'

Her face changed.

'You're seeing someone else, aren't you?'

'Okay, you're joking now.'

I came close but she pushed me away.

'Where were you last night till two in the morning then?'

'I told you, I was round Sammy's.'

'Okay,' she said, taking out her phone. 'I'll call Sammy's mum right now, see what she has to say.'

'Stop.'

'Ah...'

'Listen, last night I was...' I turned away. 'I was out gambling last night.'

'Gambling? You promised me.'

I sat down, putting my head in my hands.

'I lapsed, I'm sorry. I know I shouldn't have but, I think I might need to get some help again.'

I must have been good because within a minute she had her arm around me.

'Listen, we can work on this. You can go back to Gamblers Anonymous. You can do it, just like you did before.'

When we were first together I'd explain any sudden drug earnings as gambling wins. After all, the curse was in my family and she knew it. Then during disputes when heavies came knocking, I told her it was to do with gambling debts. It was mad, but how else could I explain the cash and the late nights? Mel's brother had died of an H overdose and she'd have never tolerated being with a guy who dealt the shit, no way. But that was all in the past. When Kellie was born I told her I was getting help, knocking it all on the head, and in a way I wasn't lying. My life was different now. Or at least it had been until last night.

'I'm glad you've been honest, Jase. That's what we promised each other. No lies. Now tell me, and be truthful, how much do you owe?'

'A hundred.'

'That's not too bad. I'll borrow it off my mum. You can pay her back in instalments. But promise me, never again. And promise you'll go back to GA.'

I promised, and we spent the next hour in the bedroom. Then I had to rush out to sign on.

Sammy took the break shot, potting two balls instantly, followed by three more.

'There you go Jase,' chalking his cue. 'Beat that.'

I potted one clean in, then messed up on the next, almost potting the black.

'Jeez, I need another drink.'

'Don't play the master if you ain't got the moves,' he smiled, wiping me off the table.

We sat and had a drink, the pool hall quiet.

'So,' I said, leaning in. 'Do you think we'll get away with it?'

'I'm pretty certain. They've got nothing on us, there's no evidence. And our alibi's sorted – we were all around Bigzy's.'

Just then Bigz strolled in wearing his mechanic's overalls.

'It's the devil himself,' Sammy patting the seat next to him.

Bigz seemed confident we were safe too.

'If it was a murder investigation the feds would be pulling out all the stops, but a failed robbery and a victim who's virtually back behind the counter? It'll soon be forgotten.' He kept talking: 'Thing is though, I was expecting big notes on that job and fixing the odd car ain't getting me nowhere. I say we start planning another earner. I know this place in Neasden, yeah...'

'Count me out,' I told him. 'I don't want to know.'

'You got any better ways of making money then?'

'Listen, don't you think that last job is saying something?'

'Like what?'

'That you're pretty crap at robbing. So leave it alone.'

Scraping back his chair he stood up.

'You fucking insulting me, blud?'

'Sit down,' Sammy told him.

'No I won't,' pointing his finger at me. 'You're just a white-boy pussy. You ain't got the balls for this kind of thing.'

I grabbed the neck of a bottle, Bigz pulling a spanner from his overalls and Sammy saying, 'Whoa, whoa, whoa!'

There was only so much of his bullshit I could stand.

My dad was half-black, but obviously that wasn't enough for this prick.

Sammy told us to grow up, allow it, you're acting like you're back in the playground.

We put down our weapons.

I shook my head and headed for the door.

'You're a prick, Bigz.'

'Fuck you, man,' kissing his lips.

I came out of the job interview, walking past the waiting room where eight others were competing for the one office position, and knew I didn't stand a chance. Look at me, all suited and booted, and for what? The interviewers had been looking down their noses at me like I was polluting their breathing space, and I don't even know why I turned up. My CV was full of make-believe, but it was as if they'd already done their research. Those three months inside were like a mark for life. But I had a family to feed and I needed a decent job. Whatever happened to giving people a chance? On the tube home I could have done with a happy pill. Then on the street I got a call from Sammy. He told me to get over to the pool hall pronto, he had something for me.

'What's with the get-up man?' he smiled as I walked in. 'You been to a wedding or something?'

'Job interview.' I said, sitting down. 'Though I might as well have told them I was a crack dealer.'

'Listen up, I've got something that's going to brighten your day. You ready?'

'Try me.'

He reached into his pocket and slapped a wad down on the table.

'Seven hundred, my man. Enjoy it.'

'What the fuck?'

'Let's just say I promised you a payday on the Cricklewood job. And when Sammy makes a promise, Sammy delivers.'

He explained how him and Bigz had gone on a little money raise last night: 'A shop in Neasden, a clean transaction. No complications. You know me J, that's how I roll.'

I felt the notes in my hand.

'I don't know if I can take this Sam – I mean, it's yours, you earned it.'

'Call it a bit of compo. Now put it away. You need it, I know you do.'

He wasn't wrong. I tucked it in my pocket, smiling now. Then I gave him a little hug.

'What can I say? Thanks man.'

'One thing though,' he said, leaning down to take a shot. 'We had to retrieve the Glock.'

'What?'

'We had to dig it back up. We needed a tool.'

I'd spent most of the day changing nappies or trying to fix our useless boiler, and now I was walking home from a Gamblers Anonymous meeting and all I wanted to do was put my feet up. As I neared the flat, Sammy pulled up in his car, looking stressed.

'Get in, J. I've been trying to call you for the past hour.'

We drove and he told me the news.

Trey Smith and the Donnelly brothers had been pulled in for the Cricklewood job. They were released on bail and most likely wouldn't be charged, but they were pissed off and wanted a pay-off. Four figures.

'How did they know it was us? I thought you told nobody?'

'I didn't, but you know how it is, word gets around.'

'You mean Bigz opened his mouth as usual.'

'Look, I don't know about you, but I've spent all my cash, so basically we're going to have to go to work again.'

'I don't believe this. Look, what if we just tell them to fuck off?'

'Stop dreaming, Jase. Trey and the D brothers are on a different level, you know that. You want me to remind you of their previous?'

I shook my head. I knew full well. We had no choice.

'Listen up. Bigz has got a job lined up for Thursday. A late-night betting shop in Kilburn. That should be our problem sorted.'

Mel had just got Kellie off to sleep, so at last I could play *Grand Theft Auto* in peace. I was just getting into it, finally ridding my mind of the D brothers and the forthcoming job, when Mel started smooching up next to me, no doubt wanting to head to the bedroom. I subtly shrugged her off, but she kept on.

'Not now!' I shouted, and she was up on her feet.

'You hardly look at me these days! It's like you don't even want to be with me anymore!'

'I'm sorry,' I told her. 'I've just got a lot on my plate.'

'Like what?'

'Work. I want to provide and I can't find any – it's doing my head in.'

She stared at me. But this time she wasn't so easily fooled.

'You're up to something. And I'm going to find out what it is.'

I sat in the car counting the seconds. Then Sammy and Bigz burst from the bookies, each carrying a loaded bag. They jumped in – Go! - I put my foot down and we were out of there. Back at Bigzy's lock-up we counted the cash. Separating Trey and the Donnelly's four large, we each had three hundred to play with. Not bad.

'So you're sure they're going to be off our back then?'

'Guaranteed,' Sammy said. 'Me and Bigz are going to drop it off tomorrow. It's good as done.'

I stayed for a beer, Bigz showing us his latest stash of dodgy goods. This time it was perfume.

'*Rogue* by Rihanna. I've got four full boxes of this shit. Smells pretty rank though. Here, Jase...'

He tried spraying me with the stuff.

'Fuck off, man!'

'You want one for your woman? Ten quid.'

'I wouldn't take that shit gratis.'

Sammy was laughing as he lit a blunt. He offered it over but I wanted to keep a clear head tonight. I was in the doghouse at the moment and needed to get back in Mel's good books.

Back home I walked in holding a bunch of flowers and a box of chocolates. After a few seconds Mel smiled. Then she got up and hugged me. I had a feeling this would work. Then suddenly she pulled away from me.

'You've been with a girl...I can smell her...I can smell the bitch!'

She threw the flowers and Milk Tray across the room.

'Trying to butter me up after seeing your bit on the side, are you? That's it, I've had enough.'

She was charging about throwing things into bags.

'I'm going back to my mum's and you can go fuck yourself – and your bitch - any time you like!'

I kept telling her it was just Bigz messing about but she didn't want to know. Within fifteen minutes her mum pulled up outside, and with Kellie in her arms and some bags she was off.

'Come back, please!'

The car pulled away. I turned to notice the spectators that had gathered, enjoying the entertainment. I spent the next few days whipping up crazy phone bills trying to persuade Mel it was all a misunderstanding. Her mum was slagging me off non-stop in the background, but in the end I won Mel round.

'Okay, maybe I'll come back this evening,' she said. 'But don't forget your GA meeting.'

'I won't, I promise, I'll be there.'

I sat back in relief. Then Sammy phoned.

'Bad news. Trey and the D's want one more pay-off. The cops are watching them and it's affecting their business.'

'Right, Sammy, from me you can tell them to fuck off.'

'Reality check, Jase. These guys won't just target you, they'll target your family. You want to risk that?'

Another job was lined up for Wednesday.

At the GA meeting a new guy was sitting in the circle, cap and hood covering most of his face. When the leader introduced him and he looked up, I got the shock of my life. It was Trey Smith. Noticing each other we both looked embarrassed. Then when it was Trey's turn to tell his tale he hardly spoke, saying he'd prefer to just listen this week, and I wasn't surprised.

'Jase, man,' he smiled, tapping my fist when we broke for coffee. 'I ain't seen you for time.'

Back at school he'd been well known for his schizo temperament, nice as pie one minute, lethal the next, but considering the circumstances he just seemed too friendly. Was he playing a game?

'Between you and me,' he said quietly, 'I don't even have a gambling problem. I mean, I use the machines just like the next guy, but you know how it is. You okay, bruv?'

'Yeah, I'm fine, I just...' Then I got straight to the point. 'Trey listen, I want to apologise for all that shit lately. You guys being hassled was the last thing we wanted. If it was up to me...'

'Hang on, you've lost me. What you on about?'

Sammy and Bigz weren't answering their phones, so I headed down the railway to Bigzy's lock-up. It was cold and late but there he was, working under a car. I had a good mind to let the jack down on him.

'Get up you fat fucker, now!' I said, kicking over a box of tools.

He wheeled himself out and stood up.

'What's up with you?'

I pushed him with both hands.

'Playing me for a fool, yeah?'

Then I swiped some shit off a shelf just to piss him off.

He lunged for me and we started thrashing it out, wrestling to and fro, something that should have happened a long time ago. Before long he was huffing and puffing and I was getting the better of him – until he grabbed a brace and got me a good one across the head. Seeing stars I staggered to the floor.

Bigz stood rooting through a drawer. Then next thing he was standing over me pointing the Glock.

'You wanna die, Jase?' he grinned, wiping blood from his face. 'I could shoot you right now, get rid of your body and nobody would ever know.'

'Go fuck yourself, Bigz.'

'Still full of it yeah?' he said, stepping closer. 'You know, maybe what you need is a fucking lesson. A nice little kneecapping. Cripple you up so you won't be strutting round so cocky anymore...'

I sprang for him. A shot hit the wall as I grabbed his arm, my fist hammering at his face until he crashed back into some car parts. The Glock clattered across the floor and I leapt for it.

Pointing the gun at him he just stood there, out of breath and laughing.

'Fair play, Jase. You win.' Then he edged closer. 'Come on man, let's call it quits. I was only fucking about anyway, put the gun down.'

'One step more and you're dead,' I warned him.

He shook his head, feigning laughter.

Then he lunged for me.

I pulled the trigger – one, two, three. Bigz dropped to his knees, his shocked eyes staring at me until he slumped face-downwards.

I watched as a pool of blood appeared by his side. Jesus Christ, I'd just killed him .I looked around. Then I thought of the money box where he'd stashed his cash the other night. I went over to the desk and opened it, several grand staring back at me.

Mel and Kellie were back home where they belonged, and Mel and I made sure to have a nice early night to make up for lost time. Things felt back to normal again.

I woke up the next morning with my mobile buzzing next to me.

'You're not going to believe this,' Sammy said between sobs. 'Bigz is dead, man...someone shot him dead.'

'No way.' Then unable to resist it I said, 'Was it the Donnelly's?'

Later that day he picked me up in his car. He told me the police were saying it could have been a robbery, but were looking at all angles.

Then he said:

'Listen, about Trey and the D brothers...'

'Forget it, Sammy. I already know.'

He looked at me about to say something, then he turned away. We pulled in by Bigzy's mum's house to give our condolences.

With little to go on and no witnesses the police hit a brick wall. It was a cold misty night and Bigzy's lock-up was tucked round the back of nowhere. Me and Sammy were soon questioned, but so were a lot of people. Bigz was a dodgy guy who had obviously upset somebody.

These things happen. They happen all the time.

ANDREW TAYLOR

18.12.13

a block no consideration
for breaks
by the tree light
hot coffee
hint of brownie
Roger's piano
remastering allows for hearing
the finest of details
quartet hint of audience
Andrew you can still send
your gifts in time for Christmas
slow drop
no needles
slow focus
at sea level
thirst for knowledge
the romance of steam
eighteen arches
we followed
that line
counted the gravel

1.1.14

puddle gather patio
chip bag blow
metal bin metal box
limited
let's go and see
the sea
what colour is the lighthouse?

the docks
send
scrap metal
four squares
public
art
recollection
string of red hearts across
bedstead
chit chat
comfort safety
image
rest

8.1.14

blackout blind
doesn't ease
the waking
beyond
a clue
to how to map
respond
a change
is given
within difficulty
is beauty
rap of drip
hum of projection
key tap
there is
never quite
a total

CRAIG GIBSON
The Faerie Boy of Leith

One O'Clock Gun is an Edinburgh based free literary
publication available in various drinking haunts in the
city. Its founder and editor is Craig Gibson and the
following story is based on true events...

The Master without Honour and a coterie of assorted
Gun veterans were drinking earnestly in the Bailie Bar
one balmy evening in late July. This was not a social
occasion, and the faces around the table were grim as
their owners discussed the latest snub to be delivered to
The Gun by the all-powerful Edinburgh International
Book Festival. Once again, Ms Lockerbie had refused
permission for The Gun to be distributed FREE in the
hallowed precincts of Charlotte Square Gardens.
According to Frau Direktor, The Gun, an Edinburgh
paper produced by and for the good people, had 'no
direct link to the EIBF'.

It was the opinion of those present that this insult must
be avenged by any means necessary, but nevertheless the
company realised that they could not achieve this goal on
their own. To send The Gun against the EIBF in a toe-to-
toe would be a brave, but ultimately doomed gesture and
would accomplish nothing. After much debate the
company agreed they would have to seek aid from
elsewhere, for they could not stand alone against the
ruthless corporate giant.

The Master's face suddenly took upon a crafty look
and, although he feared ridicule for what he was about to
suggest, he continued.

'Yes my friends, we need a powerful ally.
Unfortunately, all the literary powers-that-be in town are
in Catherine's pocket. Therefore we must turn to another

kind of aid. Something a bit out of the ordinary. Something supernatural,' he hissed for dramatic effect.

He was instantly mocked by the more rationalist members of the table, but he held up his hand and continued.

'My Grandad, who was a sailor, bequeathed to me on his deathbed a small wooden box containing a rude flute and a set of instructions written on vellum. These told of the Faerie Boy of Leith and described how the owner of the flute, in a time of crisis, could summon him if he stood on the Calton Hill when the moon was full and played a certain tune. Now, I know some of you may be familiar with Captain George Burton's account and assume it is nothing more than a fable. Well, my Grandad swore the Faerie Boy was for real and though he was a drinking man, he was never a liar. So, my friends, as it is full moon in three days time, I am going to take my flute up the Calton Hill at midnight and summon the help of all Faerieland!'

'You can't even play the flute!' the Fingersmith snorted, as the entire table broke up with guffaws and jeers.

'I'm a fucking quick learner,' the Master retorted as he swept from the bar haughtily.

Calton Hill, full moon. The Master checked his watch and saw it was a quarter to the witching hour. Swiftly, he removed the flute from his inside pocket and laid the vellum gently on the ground. With the aid of his lighter he read through the instructions once again, even though he had spent the previous three evenings memorising them. No point in taking any chances.

At the appointed time he turned around three times, widdershins, and began to play the simple tune as instructed on the manuscript. He was rather smugly congratulating himself on his new-found musical ability when he detected a slight whiff of sulphur and sensed that someone was standing behind him. He whirled around to observe the Boy, who was shaking his head in a good natured, if slightly insolent fashion.

'Gled ye could mak it, Maister Falkland. No seen ye doon the Port for a lang time syne. The bodies say ye're an Edinburgh man noo,' said the imp mischievously. 'Noo whit can ah dee for ye?'

This was all a bit much for the Master to take in all at once, but he found his mouth working as if of its own accord.

'Why have you got a Borders accent if you're the Faerie Boy of Leith, then?'

'Ah kin talk like a Leither if that wid suit ye better. But I suspect that only the Queen's English will be good enough for the Master without Honour these days,' the Boy sneered.

He was about the same height as an 11-year-old child, but his upturned nose, pointy ears and tousled hair gave him a Puck-like appearance that befitted an ambassador from Faerieland. His drum hung carelessly at his side and he twirled the beaters idly in his left hand. He was, however, dressed in the manner of a contemporary urchin: hooded top, trackie bottoms and trainers. For some reason the Master found this apparel to be the most disconcerting thing of all.

'How do you know my name? And how do I know you're for real? Those don't look like Faerie clothes to me,' he enquired, scratching his head. 'You might be an impostor.'

'I know many things, my good Master,' said the imp impatiently, 'for I've been here a long, long time.' His voice and manner belied his youthful appearance. 'And I dress how I please. Tracksuits and the like are very comfortable,' he stated curtly. His little flinty eyes narrowed suspiciously. 'I know your name and I know why you've come, for I read you as easily as a book. You want me to bang my drum and have the whole Faerie

Host descend upon Charlotte Square Gardens for the month of August. Think of it, a horde of invisible brownies and bogles, kelpies and pisgies, imps and elves, all pulling at guy-ropes, ruining readings, salting the beer, invading the Writers' Yurt and tweaking their noses, pulling their hair and stealing children. The Host unleashed against the EIBF, that is what you desire, is it not?'

The Master's eyes were afire as he nodded.

'Then you are a fool and your arrogance will be your undoing. You really thought that by playing a few notes, badly I may add, on your Grandad's flute you could command the Invisible Empire to do your bidding!'

The imp went into a fit of giggles that threatened to transform him into a child again. The Master stared at his feet, his face reddening, feeling more foolish than ever. The Boy recovered his composure and stared curiously at him as he began to turn away dejectedly.

'Hey, come back here. Don't be so downhearted. You have summoned me and I am here to help you. So listen and learn. But first of all, give me a roll-up.'

'Revenge, my good Master, is a dish best served cold,' said the Faerie Boy as he puffed contentedly on his hand-made, 'and in any case I am going to put such foolish notions out of your head by using a cunning blend of magic and common sense. Come.'

The Boy led the Master to the highest point of the hill before proceeding, much to the Master's bemusement, to piss into a small hollow, whistling all the while. A phenomenal amount of piss for one so small, mused the Master, as the Boy took at least three minutes to complete this task. The Boy let out a long, theatrical sigh of pleasure and delved his hand deeply into his pocket before bringing out a tightly clenched fist.

'Real Faerie Dust, Master Falkland, just like in the books,' teased the Boy, his eyes twinkling as he opened his hand to allow the silver substance to fall like a miniature snowstorm over the lochan of piss at his feet. 'Now look into the mirror and tell me what you see.'

The Master stepped forward dubiously and gazed into the puddle. At first all he could see was his own form with the moon behind him. However, this image gradually faded to be replaced by a scene that he knew all too well. A miniscule Charlotte Square Gardens in the sunshine. He could not help but be astonished by this spectacle and he stood transfixed by the sight of a teeny Catherine Lockerbie leading a tiny Jamie Byng by the arm in the direction of a diminutive Writer's Yurt.

'The Book Festival. The fucking Book Festival!' gasped the Master looking up. 'But tell me – which festival am I looking at? Last year's, or this which has still to pass?'

'Ha! Then you've already grasped the first lesson. You can't tell, can you? As a matter of fact, nor can I. You see – same shit, different year. Same tents, corporate logos, same old faces doing the rounds. The garden mobbed as usual. Maybe you understand a bit better now. Look into the mirror again – the EIBF is strictly a 'bums on seats, laddie' organisation. A winning formula you might say, and one of which The Gun has no part. You have nothing to offer that is of any value to them. That's it, stare into the mirror and face the truth. The Gun is a free press, a gift to literary Edina, and as the EIBF's entire philosophy appears to involve nothing more than vulgar commerce, you are anathema to them.'

The Boy swept his hand over the mirror and the vision vanished. The Master shook his head slowly and smoked a pipe of pot thoughtfully whilst the Faerie Boy helped himself to more tobacco. After a few minutes silence the Master was forced to admit that the Boy had it sussed and expressed this verbally.

'What are we to do then?' he enquired.

'With regard to the festival? Nothing at all. In fact go and see a few shows, maybe. I would recommend Rushdie – that man's got balls. Above all, don't let it spoil your fun or interfere with your mission. The month of August can bear fruit if you look in the right places. Seek and ye shall find etcetera. With regards to The Gun, as a Leith man you should know this – persevere! You and your colleagues are going to enjoy the ride if you stick to the true path, and you will be a happy man before your beard is grey. The Gun has endured many trials during its brief life – treachery, jealousy, poverty, and indifference, to name but a few. These trials have only strengthened the resolve and integrity of all involved. You will succeed on your own terms, but you must persevere!'

'Can you show me our future in the mirror?' asked the Master eagerly and with much anticipation.

'No. Too much too soon, I'm afraid. To look upon that would be akin to looking upon the face of the Most High – for such knowledge would burn you! Just heed my words, laddie. Keep the faith and above all persevere! Now listen to these Leithers who succeeded on their own terms.'

With these words the Boy took a step back and began to beat out a simple rhythm upon his drum. The beat became infectious and the Master, despite himself, clapped his hands enthusiastically as the Boy began to sing 'The Joyful Kilmarnock Blues' by The Proclaimers. However, to the Master's delight, it was the voice of Craig Reid that issued from the Boy. And wait – was it just the wind or could he really hear Charlie's backing vocals and guitar? The Master closed his eyes rapturously and joined in with gusto.

The wisdom of Craig and Charlie had long been held sacred by the Master and his voice soared as they chanted the lyrics together.

As the song drew to a close, the Master found himself drowsy and he was unable to combat the waves of tiredness which had begun to overwhelm him. More Faerie magic, he thought contentedly. He lay down, and as he drifted off, the last thing he heard was the Boy gently murmuring in his Borders voice:

'Ah'll have tae leave ye noo, Maister Falkland. But ah'll leave ye a wee token as ye've been a very clever chiel. Ye'll persevere noo, mind.'

The Master awoke at dawn and was immediately aware of an object lying at his feet. 'Twas a beautiful Pringle sweater with a red body, midnight-blue sleeves and boasting a lion rampant for decoration on the chest. On closer inspection, the Master discovered that the sweater had been signed by the brothers Reid and bore the legend PERSEVERE!

This garment was far too precious to be worn on any man's back, he judged. Instead, he would mount the Boy's gift on a T-bar and use it as the Gun standard, just like the Faerie Flag of Dungavel. It would serve them well in the coming month. As the Master left the hill clutching his precious memento, he was reminded of the children's programme, Mr Benn, and he allowed himself a brief chuckle: God knows what the others are going to make of this.

THOMAS McCOLL

CHIP SHOP AQUARIUMS

Last night,
at the local chip shop

the server,
thrusting his bare arms
into the vats of boiling oil

screamed at the cold, cruel world
that made him go insane,

and like a million piranha fish
in schools of bubbling frenzy,
the vicious viscous liquid
ate his flesh.

In chip shop aquariums,
the fish are dead
but the liquid in each tank is alive.

This all makes sense
in a world gone mad.

KOSMO VINYL
INTERVIEW

The following New York conversation was published in PUSH 16.

Joe England: Some readers won't know who you are, but others most definitely will. So to those not in the know, who is Kosmo Vinyl?

Kosmo Vinyl: I would now describe myself as an artist, West Ham supporter, music enthusiast, family man and Londoner turned New Yorker. I am best known for my years working with Ian Dury and The Blockheads and The Clash.

How did working with those artists come about?

I had managed to pester my way into a job at the recently esatblished Stiff Records, doing whatever was asked of me. Ian Dury had just put out 'Sex & Drugs & Rock & Roll' on Stiff and having established myself as a bit of a loudmouth, I was forunately given the job of promoting it. Ian and I hit it off, and I ended up working with just him – publicity, promotion, planning – pretty much everything that didn't have t do with money. Later I moved camps to work with The Clash, with the idea of seeing them reach their potential.

That must have been an exciting time. Band doing the London pub circuit and then *New Boots & Panties* hitting the scene. It's up there with all the great album titles and such a cool

iconic cover too. Is there anything you want to add about Ian that hasdn't been said already?

Ian actually didn't have a band when he made 'Sex & Drugs' and 'New Boots'. Back then he was in partnership with Chaz Jankel. The Blockheads came together for the Stiff Tour. I didn't realise at the time, but Ian was really an artist. He had studied at The Royal College of Art as a painter and while teaching at Canterbury he switched mediums. Instead of paint and canvas, or pencil on paper, he started using words and music. The reason his stuff is so unique is that he approached the whole thing, music recording and live perforamance, from a totally different angle to most.

I think it worked because whether you liked what he was doing or you didn't, fact was, this guy was genuine. So how far did your involvement with Ian go?

I was very involved within, what we were going to do and how we were going to do it. At first it was getting the presentation right and getting known. As it became more successful there was a lot of deciding what to do and what not to do. How to retain identity and integrity. On the road Ian and I shared a room and we were rarely interested in anything else. Back then there was just the three of us. Me, Ian and his minder/neighbour – former bank robber Fred 'Spider' Rowe from Battersea. We were like brothers. Me the youngest, Ian in the middles and Spider eldest – and you'll note I say *eldest* and not *wisest*!

Sounds to me like the three of you were proper old school villainy. Bank jobs aside, how long were you with with Ian and Spider?

The best part of three years. From 'Sex & Drugs' up until after 'Reasons To Be Cheerful' – I think one of the best things I did was to convince Ian to bring Wilko Johnson into The Blockheads. Wilko said he was going to hang up his guitar and to me that was out of the question.

Was Wilko really that serious back then about jacking it all in?

I think he was skint and he didn't think he was getting anywhere with his band. How long it would have lasted if he had, I have no idea. I didn't really know him that well, he seemed serious about it though to me.

What happened recently with Wilko Johnson's health, the way he flciked the V sign at cancer, gave a lot of hope to many.

Didn't Charles Bukowski say, 'What matters most is how you walk through the fire,'? Well Wilko certainly walked through it.

Ian Dury seems to have been from a similar mindset, albeit his boat on the lake got called in. Were you still in touch through the years?

Ian played his last gig at the London Palladium and just before he died he told a mutual pal, 'It's alright, the body's fucked but the spirits strong.' Says it all really. We exchanged the odd note and letter, but I don't think I could have handled seeing him right at the end. Just too much for me.

I can understand that. Anyway mate. The Clash. Your name has always been closely associated with his great band. What's the story there? I even heard you managed them at one time?

Well with The Clash it was always a case of doing whatever needed doing – publicity, plannuing, management, MC on stage, barber, boot rental, whatever. When I joined up with them FULL ON, which was before *London Calling* came out, I felt they were a bit cornered and punching below their weight. I encouraged them to take on the challenge of the big time and compete on the world stage. I thought that they were the best rock n roll band in the world and the job at hand was to get the rest of the world to agree.

So what exactly was the plan, how did you get them motivated, get them punching above their weight? Because when *London Calling* did come out, everything went up many levels. Did you have to bang heads together?

No banging heads together and I don't want to create an impression that I was responsible, but I was part of the team that tried to pull it off and to some degree succeeded. It was a combination of things. Their playing had improved dramatically and they were making the music they really wanted to make and damn the consequences; everyone upped their game on all fronts. We got everything a little more strategic and thought out. Sometimes the sum of the parts is greater than the ingredients. You create something bigger, get that extra dimension. A whole bunch of people contributed, bit of course, it was Joe, Mick, Paul and topper that were the vital ingredients.

I think you are the kind of good guy who would say all that but had more involvement that you'd care to admit, but you were the man who shouted at thousands at Shea Stadium while introducing The Clash: 'You all sound like you are half asleep!' Seriously, that was some expereince though. Any thoughts still with you about that day?

What amazes me now is that it happened at all. It's hard for me to believe that I did that. Don Letts filmed them going to the gig and we hired a car from a bloke that used to drive Marilyn Monroe and I got left back, they drove off with film crew in tow, and I thought, fuck me, I'd better get to the gig! So I hailed a yellow taxi, jumped in and told the driver: Shea Stadium and sharpish!

You didn't have any 'where's your ticket mate?' hassle when you finally turned up then?

Fortunatley not – I was expected!

Right mate. Here we go. From Shea stadium to Olympic Stadium. Your thoughts on that move in a second. So before that, how did you get to support West Ham United?

Family Joe! So no choice. And that is as it should be.

Amen to that brother.

Well, my old man supported West Ham as did both my grandads. Irons in the blood! And I'm proud to say both my boys support West Ham too.

Now this bloke you know. This Mick Jones out of The Clash. He's QPR. I'd seen him one time coming out of Loftus Road all moody-faced even though they'd beaten us. You know him well, so do you feel sorry for Mick right now, all that suffereing he has been through and on it goes – or is it, get over yourself just like at West Ham, as we have always had to?

I have a lot of respect for Mick and his following of QPR. He has stuck with it and let's face it, he's not going to get a lot of glory out of Loftus Road is he? He's never wavered and although they can be a poxy team they are HISpoxy team. Well, his and Glen Matlock's. He's a proper West London boy and I've lived over that way myself because of The Clash, often travelling to and from Bow.

Paul Simonon was The Clash for me. All the way. He had a recent exhibition at the ICA. I never realised Paul was a proper biker. But he can paint. From a distance, some of work looked like it was in HD. Now, what I want to know is this. Did he support West Ham or QPR? And if it was Spurs, then I don't want to know, so just answer – he was just a focussed biker/bassist.

Paul was into painting before he joined The Clash and he's been a part of the british Motorcycle scene for donkey's years – there's a whole tribe of them. But when Paul was a kid he supported Spurs.

Oh here we go.

He supported Spurs because he liked Jimmy Greaves. He liked Jimmy Greaves so much he saved his odd job money to buy a giant poster of Greavsie. It cost him a small fortune and he only had it a short while and then Spurs sold Jimmy Greaves to West Ham. And yeah, that was it for Paul. Bollocks to football. I don't think he ever supported a team again. He used to play regularly. But I don't know if he still does. Must ask him next time I see him.

This time last year Stepney born and bred Jah Wobble was in PUSH. He said when Greavsie went to West Ham, him and his mates went over Upton Park so that they could still watch him play, and I thought that was something special, to do that. Follow a player so committed like that. Now you say you're 3473 miles from the Boleyn Ground on your West Ham Art blog. What is is called and exactly what is it?

My West Ham Art blog is called *Is Saitch Yer Daddy* and it's after an old piece of graffiti (painted with a brush) that could be viewed from the District Line en route to Upton Park near Bromley by Bow tube station. I think that there's a TV studio there now. It actually used to say – *Is Switch A Daddy* – but I was concerned someone else might have used it. To me it represents the pre-gentrified East London I knew as a kid.

What was your first West Ham game?

1965/66. At home to Blackburn Rovers. We won 4-1. Absolute magic. And my favourite game until we stuffed Sunderland 8-0 a few years later. My dad always took me on the Chicken Run at first, in tribute to his old man, but when he couldn't go – he was a bricklayer and often worked Saturday's when he could – I went with my uncle and cousin. I had a claret and blue painted stool to stand on and if it was packed then they would pass the kids down the front – almost like body surfing.

I know many who watched their football from the Chicken Run in the 50/60s and I've always been jealous. And now, moving forward, West Ham United are moving to Stratford. I used to back the move but now I'm not so sure. What are your thoughts?

As I have said before, when it happens I will cry like a baby, but I am all for moving Joe. It's the future and it's what's best for the club. I'd be in favour of redevoping the ground if it was possible, but I can't see how it would ever be done. The layouts all wrong. I have no idea what will become of the Upton Park area post West Ham but on the other side of the coin, accepting 21st century football as the money mad industry that it is and cannot be stopped by West Ham staying at The Boleyn, well look at the possibilities for a Stratford based West Ham. Considering the area and transport hub at its feet, managed properly, West Ham could become the biggest supported club in London, and without having to leave East London. Trust me, most of the original Brooklyn population have still not recovered from the Dodgers being sold to Los Angeles. But as you're asking, Ronnie Lane of The Small Faces/The Faces came from Stratford and that makes the move King Kosher to me.

JIM GIBSON
Skeb Again?

Eight o'clock and me and Jake were waiting outside the shop. Newstead's only a small mining village with no major landmarks, so the closed shop was the only place that we could think to set up as a meeting point. All we'd wanted was a ten bag, a quick smoke and to chill out. It was a Saturday night, but when you're skint you can't really party hard, especially in a village like this.

We knew he'd be late. They always were. We'd been waiting since seven and now it was beginning to get to us. Jake sat on the railings and I paced on the road, both in silence. Every car that approached was inspected with a keen eye; they all quickly drove off with a worried look at our intense stares.

Finally, he arrived and I went over to the window, the tenner clasped relentlessly in my hand, ready for the switch-over. Before I could speak the man in the passenger side opened his mouth.

'Get in.'

I did this without thought. This might sound stupid to you but anyone who's been in this situation has been in the back of these cars a thousand times and is usually dropped off just around the corner. It was all normal until he passed the train station's deserted street and carried on driving.

'Here'll do, wont it?' I asked.

'Were just gonna get a couple of ounces from Skeb then we'll 'ave yer ten, yeh.' I only knew the man in the front as Whitey. I didn't want to know more.

I knew Skeb though. Everyone in the village did. He's the one who's outside when you hear a commotion. The one who smashed into the wall with his car. And the one who takes more holidays a year than anyone else, if you get my drift. Needless to say, I was nervous about the situation. But I'd been in these kinds of places before. I knew how to hold it. As they pulled up and got out of the car so did I.

The door was knocked and the house entered.

I saw straight away what their new hobby was and tried to blandly fade into the back of the room. This couldn't go quick enough. I couldn't take in what was being said.

I was the only one left standing as my associates who I had arrived with, sat down and picked up the foil straws and plates. They inhaled long and deep, burning the bottom of the foil.

Skeb spotted me. He had only been two years above me at school and we'd had all that you do as a youngster in a small village. We'd had laughs and fights, but that was before.

'Johno! I dint see you wi' these lot. You wanna toot?'

I shook my head.

'No thanks mate, only here 'cos these were gonna sort me out a bud.'

'This is better than the piffest bud you'll get mate, tek a seat.'

I sat down and felt a buzz in me pocket. I knew it was Jake so I ignored the vibrations; this lot weren't in a state to notice.

'Can ya remember when Alex fuckin' nabbed yer hat and ya banged him?' Skeb laughed as he said this but Alex was his brother and he'd never mentioned it before. Not since he had that word with me anyway.

He stood up and looked down at me laughing.

I mustered a chuckle.

'That were ages ago.'

He must've sensed the worry. I saw him breathe it in through his nose like the purest air.

'Yeah but ya fuckin' decked me little bruvva man.' He sounded calm but I could see the intent in his eyes.

'I was smashed mate, dint know what I were doing, did I.'

There was quiet as Skeb crumbled another brown rock onto the foil. The rest of 'em looked between the two of us with glazed over eyes.

Skeb seemed unaffected by the smack as he pulled long and hard through the curled foil tube. He spoke, keeping the smoke in his lungs as long as he could, so his voice croaked out. 'What would you do if *I* took your hat?' He let the cloud out with a splutter.

'I dunno mate.' My heart was racing but all of the blood felt like it was gone from my face. I couldn't tell if it was the fumes or if this was just too much. Looking back it was definitely too much, the fumes wouldn't have helped much though. The thick musty smell clung to my nostrils and each breath seemed to lack in vital oxygen. Skeb stood up with that grin chiselled into his cheeks. He'd always had that grin since he was younger and it'd often scared me as a boy but now it was more malicious. The person around it had grown and the worries that came with him just as much. It felt uncanny. As we had aged so had the level of darkness and torment. He wasn't pressuring me into a shit Pokemon card deal now. He wasn't 'borrowing' my *Game Boy*.

He walked over and pulled my flatpeak hat from my head. I stood up and looked at the grinning faces all silently cheering the lion on for their enjoyment. I probably shouldn't have stood up but I did. Being a couple of inches taller than him, he didn't like it.

He placed it on his head at a slant and said 'come n ger it then', as he grabbed an empty bottle of vodka from the mantelpiece, holding it by its neck.

'Nah mate, keep it. I'm off.'

But I didn't move. I couldn't bring myself to turn my back on him and I'd only got that hat that day. My fucking birthday of all days.

'I only got it today mate. It's my birthday present.'
Fuck knows why I was trying to appeal to the better side
of a lad who's just smoked a ten of smack.

They all had a lifeless chuckle. Apart from Skeb,
his laugh was as raucous as ever. 'Go on, ya can 'ave it if
ya just tek it.' The bottle hung in his hand and his
knuckles appeared stained white.

I was a child again.

'C'mon Skeb, don't be shady mate.'

He pushed me with the butt of the bottle.

'Take. The. *Fucking*. Hat.'

...I grabbed the fucking hat...

I clasped it in my hands.

In the same motion I bolted.

I jumped the settee standing on Whitey's arm that
was leaning on the rest in the process, but I don't think
he noticed. Then I was in the kitchen, scampering. All of
these council houses have the same layout so I knew the
route for my escape.

Through the door the cold night hit me. The silence
was too much. The yellow streetlamps made the cold
night colder. I ran up the deserted street as my adrenaline
fuelled blood pumped around my body.

My heart was thumping through my ears but I still
heard Skeb shout.

'I'm gonna fuckin' get ya this time Johno!'

I didn't know what I'd done. I'd have cried if I
thought it would've helped.

Round the back of the youth club I found a dark
corner and sat huddled up.

Jake answered his phone straight away.

'Where the fuck are you? I'm freezing me tits off
ere!'

'Mate! I'm hiding round the back o' the youthie, ya
gotta come. Skebs after me n I'm shittin meself.'

191

'What ya on about ya twat!'

'Jake seriously, I dunno what to do.'

'How comes he's after ya?'

'Cos I smacked Alex like a fuckin year ago!'

'I told ya that were trouble when ya did it.'

We were to meet at a safe spot. The tree I'd known for years, the one that I could traverse blindfolded. Every knot and crack in the bark was another story I could tell.

I had to crawl through the now overgrown shrubbery that hadn't been trodden for many years. I crawled through the nettles and seasonally browned bracken, covering as much as my body with clothing as I could.

Inside the tepee, I laid on my back and gazed up into eternity. This tree was a plane, a bus, a zoo, park, swing, skyscraper, anything and everything at one point and no-one else knew its magic. I pictured myself up in the branches, driving the plane, my younger cousins behind me pointing out the sights and enjoying the ride. But those years weren't constant smooth flying. We'd often hit turbulence.

This time Skeb walked into our den, a scrawny lad with only half a mouth-full of teeth and no t-shirt. He seemed to have dirt patched all over his body, snot dangling from his nose and smelt of sour milk. He didn't always have these problems all at once, but in my head he did this time.

He stuck his stick up at us and shot so I got out of the tree to see what he wanted.

'What's wi' the coons Johno. Dirty bastards.'

Skeb preached as he spat on the floor. He sounded like his dad.

'Don't Skeb, they're me cousins.'

He pushed me out of the way.

'Hey Pakistani, does your muvva ave a fanny?'

I got up and pushed him, making him laugh in hysterics.

'Does it smell? Snhh snhhh FUCKIN ELL!'

He was holding his stomach as he laughed and my cousins were sat up in the tree looking down, their faces sombre and helpless.

They were from nice places.

I'd had enough.

'Fuck off Skeb.' I pushed him.

He cracked me in the mouth straight away; my tooth flew out.

We rolled on the floor, punching, grabbing, choking, pulling, twisting. My cousins ran for it and I realised he's the kind to never give in. Why the fuck would he?

I left my tooth and ran.

Then I heard him.

'Jake! Where's yer fuckin' bum boy?'

They were around the corner but in the silent streets you could hear everything.

'I dunno mate, I aint seen him. Just off to me Mammars aren't I.'

I heard a smash.

'Ahrr! What the fuck Skeb!'

'Tell the cunt I'm gonna kill him!'

He was coming my way now; I could hear him on the dirt cutting. Each step had a louder rasp than the last. The steps were quick. I should have thought about it in hindsight but your brain is irrational in these situations. My phone went off. That bastard Jake should have thought about what he was doing!

'Well, well, well Johno ya fuckin little prick.'

He was coming now and this time I'd had it.

He got through the nettles quicker than I had, the smack probably absorbing the stings. And as his head poked through the tree, with that grin still set in stone, I got the first crack in; a downward punch to the side of the face that knocked him straight down.

My heart raced and when I saw the hatchet in his hand, still clenched tight as he landed on his hands and knees, I knew I didn't have a choice.

I hit him again, this time on the back of the head following through – all of my weight behind my swing – and he went down further.

I clenched my fist, I could feel the bones bent, broken, my hand bleeding.

I looked around, panting hard as I scanned for an answer. I saw my tooth lying to the side of a large root. I saw my *Game Boy* that had never been returned. Going further through my life I saw my new bike in a broken mess, his face staring through my window when me Mam was out.

I saw my girlfriend in tears when he forced it on her. I saw my car with CUNT keyed in the side.

He was always, always there to ruin everything.

I didn't even want to know the prick. I wanted him to fuck off for good and I didn't think twice now. I picked the big fucking rock up and slammed it down on his head and then I laughed. It was a hysteria, a euphoria, a joy and I didn't give a flying fuck.

I spat on his body and walked out with a swagger. The grin carved into my face felt like it would never leave. I laughed, kicked bottles and hooted with joy, not knowing where I was going but not caring one bit.

I never found out what he was thinking when he died. I never knew he saw the secret handshake I taught him, the manhunt in the woods – not knowing that he took it too far – playing FIFA on my PS2, sneaking over and playing with my dog in the garden and letting it lick his face. He wasn't thinking of his dad's iron fist, his brother's constant guile, his dog food dinners when they'd all fucked off and left him.

A child.

TIM WELLS

There But For The Grace
of Bauhaus

The beige vomit
trailed down her front
sits vivid
against the black
of her coat.

Nightbuses
are indeed
a fantasy world.

The spatters
on her faux fur collar
smize.

Though she is fierce,
unrepentant
and glorious,
in her drunkenness

the puke in her hair
makes it difficult
to commit.

The stranger
sat next to me
must think the same
for she smiles
and we both laugh.

I stand for my stop
and she whispers
'get home safe.'

The goth
heaves
into a newspaper.

David Cameron's face
looks appalled.

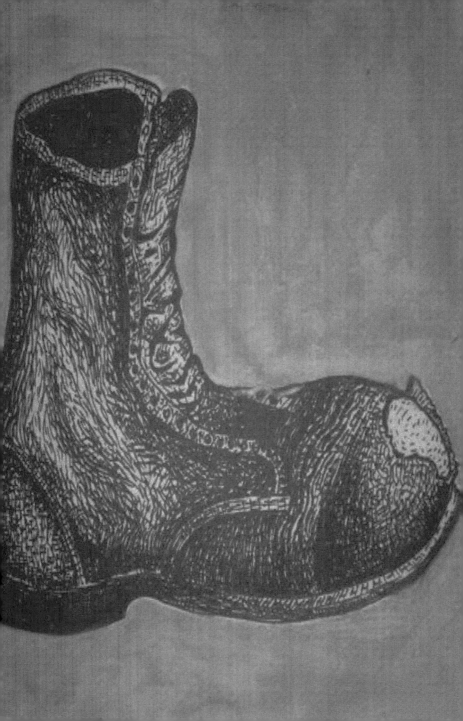

GARY BUDDEN
Up and Coming

Nights like this. It's all about this. On my own, somewhere out there in the real world I don't add up to much. There's something missing from the equation and too much doesn't make sense. Just keeping my head above water, sometimes drowning, definitely not waving. But here, I float. Tonight's the last night I'll ever stand here doing this. The last night at The Stockwell Arms before: all change, *this service terminates here*. The décor, the demographic, the price of the beer, everything. It's an uneasy feeling, being here in this moment, right now, right here in the present, knowing that when I wake tomorrow with the inevitable hangover it'll be the past, already a memory, a place we talk about fondly in the past tense until even the stories fade like photographs left out in the sun. The crowd's even more unruly than usual. Not a surprise. No-one's getting barred tonight. I'm standing at the bar chatting with Canadian Dave, Simon and his missus Ade, and some mate of theirs from Bristol, Jess. She's a bit younger than us. Her boots look new, polished to a brilliant shine. I get a sense of communion from these nights, a shared feeling and commonality that can be embarrassing when first encountered. The first time I found this, and I'm not ashamed to say it, I felt this surge inside, better than any drug I'd ever done. Like I'd found something I never even knew I was missing. A long time ago now, that was. But it was the first time things made any fucking sense. A place where I didn't feel alone. A place I didn't want to leave. Trust me on this one – it was beautiful.

I'm waiting for the barmaid to appear, tapping a beer mat on the bar as I look around. The men and women here, whose ages straddle generations (and here that's OK, it really is), they're all here for one reason. The older men and women, pushing well into their thirties, believe they've seen it all before and are eager to let everyone know; they've seen a lot, sure, their tats are starting to fade and blur a little, but I reckon they've still got a thing or two to learn. I should know; I'm one of them.

Then there's ones even older, they're *proper* old, pushing or jumping clean over the half-century, the ones who can remember 'Do They Owe Us A Living' first time round, the ones who can talk about free festivals that really were free and a world that seems, in retrospect at least, less codified. Some of them are arrogant pricks to be honest, reminding you that they were here first and don't you forget it son. But most of them are decent blokes (and it is, I'm sad to say, mainly blokes), in it for life, and there's this sense of continuity I get when I speak to them that I love. I think of myself twenty to thirty years down the line telling wide-eyed young ones about the old bloke *I knew* who'd seen Crass first hand. No way, I imagine they'll say. Maybe they won't give a shit though. For the good ones, time's softened their arrogance, mainly, but the booze has taken its toll on a significant minority. It's true, there's no denying it. It's a risk we all run. I'm as bad as any of them at times. Pint in hand on a splintery pub table in the English summer sun, just before a gig kicks off inside, that's fucking heaven to me. As I've gotten older it's only become more true.

Then there's the young ones, like Jess, showing off the fresh tattoos for all to see, skin still red and sore, their leather jackets maybe a bit too clean, badges yet to rust pinned in place and patches sewn all over. The new Doc Martens buffed to within an inch of their life. I did all that myself, of course I did. I always veered towards the skin side of the whole punk thing, took a lot of pride in the way I'd turn myself out on gig nights, jeans clean and well-fitting, boots shined and making me feel ten foot tall, Harrington or Ben Sherman over a tight black tee with some anarcho band across the front, or if I was going proper smart, then a navy or crimson Fred Perry buttoned up to the neck. I was never one of those Nazi cunts, let me tell you now. But it was like the uniform of my real life; jokingly I called the gear I wore to work, or when I went to go and see my mum and dad, my civvies. I guess I had a point to prove, to myself more than anyone, and in those clothes I felt like *me*. When you find something in this world that actually means a damn thing, you cling on for dear life. You commit to it. There's a dignity to that.

I know a lot of folks who think it's juvenile. That's something that gets me. Really niggles, you know? If your overriding passion in life is, like, paintings or books or films or fishing or even the fucking footy, then it's alright to be into that, with a blinding passion, for your whole life. With music it's different somehow. A young man's game, the world reckons. I've still never got my head fully round that one. Less booze and drugs and fights at the galleries and the poetry readings I guess; but then I've met a lot of poets and writers and let me tell you they can cane it and drink up there with the best of them. Saw some of them go down k-holes they could never climb back out of, or become cocaine cunts nobody could bear to be around. Or they believed all that shite about Dylan Thomas and Bukowski and the rest of the drinkers with a writing problem. Sad really. The song said ignorance was the British disease, but trust me, it's the pints and powder.

The young ones have the look and thrill, recent converts. I envy them that; you can't ever get it back. Not all of them will go the distance of course. They've got a good decade of guilt-free enjoyment before they've got to start thinking, do they really like this? and is this any way for an adult, someone in their thirties/forties/fifties to behave? That's a choice they've yet to make and it's an enviable position. They're the ones who'll buy the copies of *Magnesium Burns* and *Frontline* and *Punk Positive* and read them cover-to-cover. The ones who don't seem to quite believe that me and my mates were there up at The Balustrade before the bastards sold the place and the developers were let in. The people who turned it into flats and a fucking Costa coffee. I swear the council were nobbled.

These are the facts and it's something I'm seeing more and more as I get older. I feel a responsibility to remember these things. Like if I don't remember and dig out the photos and say, yeah I was there and it was like this, then it may as well never have happened. When I went down to see Simon and Ade a few weeks back, down in Kent, he dug out a load of pics of all of us up at The Balustrade. Good times. All of us thinner and with sillier haircuts. One pic was creased in this way that split Ade from head to navel, and it's an image I can't get out my head for some reason. It was on Balustrade Street, in case you're wondering about the name.

Finally the barmaid appears with a sweaty smile and she's either overworked, pissed or high, but whatever, it's fine. Tonight's the last night and no-one cares. I order a round of drinks, ciders for the lot of us, passing the glasses over a sweating sea of people to Simon who takes them to the table we've managed to secure. I hand Canadian Dave his pint and he nods seriously in thanks. I fight my way out of the scrum at the bar, cider slopping over my Fred Perry.

The gigs, the London ones at least, all seem to be getting pushed further and further out. I can talk of a time when all this stuff happened in Hackney and Brixton, even Islington, but now I find myself standing in venues where the term shithole would be an aspiration, in Tottenham or Deptford or bloody Tufnell Park where it's impossible to get to when the Northern Line goes down, which it always does. It's not right. Now even Deptford's getting tarred with the *up-and-coming* brush. How the hell did that happen?! When I'm feeling a bit paranoid, I call it social cleansing by stealth. Maybe that's a bit much, but there's something in it. And it's not even that stealthy. It's brazen.

When I see punks spark-out on dirty mattresses, pissing up against the walls of venues or openly drinking shop-bought cans inside the venue, I want to slap them. There's a group of them outside now on the wall, slurping down Scrumpy and smoking Superkings. I want to shake some sense into them and know it would do no good. Was I ever any better?

This modern blankness seeps into everything. This nihilism. Life became much harder and at the same time a belief in anything better became a kind of embarrassment. Get back to the eighties, John, where you belong! my mates and family laugh. They're going too far back anyway; I came up in the 90s. In '89 I was only twelve years old. Spiritually though, Susie said, you belong somewhere around 1984. It was probably true and contributed to the break-up, no doubt about it.

I'm no good at this constant erasure and daily amnesia. I need a timeline. I need to know history didn't end. So, less Pistols, more One Way System. Give me a future and all that.

I squeeze into the booth next to Jess, Canadian Dave opposite, Simon and Ade wedged into a corner.

You better not need a piss for the next twenty minutes, I say.

They laugh.

I pull out my tobacco tin, set it down on the cider-sticky table. Before I've even started rolling, Jess pipes up and asks:

Can I nick a fag off you?

Course you can.

Nice one.

We push through the crowd outside, into the small patch of concrete that passes as the outdoor drinking area and onto the pavement in front of the pub. The group necking their tins of Scrumpy Jack are still sat on the wall. Some of them will be out here all night, won't even bother paying to come into the gig. It irritates me.

Never been to this venue before, Jess says in a rolling West Country accent.

Your timing's impeccable, I say, lighting our cigarettes.

I exhale a cloud of blue smoke. As I do a woman passes me, pushing a buggy. I recognise her. My neighbour, Lucy.

Alright Lucy.

Oh, hello John. I didn't know you came here?

All the time. Last night tonight. Shame.

Well, good to see you, sorry I've got to dash, this little one has been keeping me busy, you know.

She smiles a tired smile.

I look at the sleeping child. Jess smiles. Lucy looks awkward, scans the crowd of drunks and black jackets, clouds of blue cigarette smoke hanging motionless in the air.

See you soon, I say.

Sometimes I look in the mirror in the morning for longer than necessary. John Whitefield, born '77, one failed marriage, no kids, greying stubble, keeping my hair at a respectable length. I don't go full skin these days. People will just think I'm another white bloke going bald. Ten years I've lived round here, and nearly everything I loved about the place has gone. I've changed too, I know that, but The Stockwell Arms going feels like the end of something. I find myself entertaining fantasies of leaving the city for good. Woods and hills and rivers and that. At times I'm even tiring of my own interests, and that's a dreadful thing. Punk to me meant at least some kind of ideology, a belief in something, not this creeping nihilism I see around me. Like the world's knackered, burnt out, in some post-ideological freefall.

I'm not saying this is entirely a new thing. There was always an aspect of that; the chaos punks who believed all the no future crap and could only see as far ahead as their next pint. I read a book about this kind of thing. Depressed hedonism was the term. I'm seeing a lot of depressed hedonists these days; and not just the punks and skins (we're so few after all). If I head up the Kingsland Road on a Friday night there's hundreds of them out and about, kids and even proper grownups with their knocked-together looks, hotch-potch aesthetics grave-robbed from subcultures that once meant something. Including *my* culture. If I see one more Black Flag t-shirt I think my head's going to explode.

Not that I head up Kingsland Road much these days. I don't have anything against the hipsters really, and I tend not to cross paths with many of them on a day-to-day basis. But they look so fucking lost to me. Oddly, I feel like they've given up. Like they've seen the future and know it's boring and fucked. I follow something of a uniform, I know that, but I never said I was an individual.

I think about how we all just inhabit roles that exist without us. Like when I was a snotty teen punk-skin I was *me*, sure, but I also fitted into a role and someone else's idea of what that thing should be, and I saw others that way too. We all talk about individuality, about how it's the thing to aim for and the thing to be celebrated and so on. But if I'm honest I think that's bollocks. Where does it leave family for a start? And we all want to belong. Be a part of something. I'm happy to say I'm me, but I'm also a part of this thing that's bigger than me and I feed it and it feeds me. And beyond this little sub-culture then I'm a part of my street, the city I live in, part of the country, part of the whole world. I'm sounding like a hippy now, but it's true.

Now a lot of the thick-as-pigshit skins and the crusty punks out of their heads on whatever powder they've scored, they won't think in these terms. I've met my fair share of narcissists over the years, trust me, people who thought they were true individuals. But I've thought about this issue long and hard as I've got older, and the stuff I thought I'd grow out of just didn't fade away. I don't feel like I'm immature; but is that an assessment only others can make? There I go again. The bar room philosopher, like an inarticulate Frankie Stubbs.

The young punks and skins have modern technology on their side. Now on that one, I'm not sure I envy them. It seems counter-intuitive, I know, but I think they've gained something but lost a lot fucking more. Maybe this is just the grumbling of an older man. Like every old git, ever, has spouted. In the early days of the scene, it's true, tracking down this music and knowing this history was a challenge. Even when I was young it was difficult, but we always found a way and maybe that's the point. This ease of access, this clear difference between the three generations, it's a problem at times. All people, in all cultures, everywhere, are expected to earn their stripes somehow and in this sense of discovering the culture, younger people do have it easier. But, still, it always comes back to the unanswerable question just what it is that makes a person like *this* and not *that* and the whole beautiful mystery of sub-culture is forever up for debate. And I could have done with eBay and YouTube and Spotify when I was young; the music I can get now blows my mind. It makes me think about what person I would've been had I had all this stuff when I was a nipper; would I have been happier, more broad-minded, or exactly the same? Remembering those pre-internet days makes me already feel like something of a relic. There'll come a time when there's no-one alive who will know a world without it.

*

We're back at the table sipping cider. You can guess what's happening to The Stockwell Arms. Someone made the owner an offer that was too good to refuse. It must be way past the million mark for a gaffe like this one. Frankly I'd take the money and run too. Who wouldn't? This is real life we're talking about. But it's a crying fucking shame because I knew what would happen to the place, I just knew it. Canadian Dave is telling the table how the whole place is getting gastro'd with a few luxury flats above as a sop to some abstract idea of 'affordable housing'.

Sign of the times, man, he says, sign of the times, and fiddles with his black cap. Always turned out head to toe in black is Canadian Dave, usually with some metalhead t-shirt with a near-indecipherable font spelling out a name pushing the definition of bad taste. Today we have: Desecrated Nun. I almost laugh, and I say, I told you this would happen. But there's no joy in being right. Times like this I wish I didn't have a fucking clue about how the world works.

It's a real shame, says Jess, looking thoughtfully into her drink.

You lot should move to Kent, says Simon. I'm telling you. London's over.

Shut up Simon, says Ade and lightly slaps his face.

He's smiling, and I know he's half-joking, but for a long second I feel the pull just to run to the nearest station, jump on the first train out of this sinking city. To do something, anything, else.

Shall we go in? I ask, draining my pint.

IAN CUSACK
Crossroads

Tuesday morning. Usual rendezvous in The Gloucester with Stevie and Aldo for a couple of early liveners. Always a canny day on the peeve is Tuesday. You've had a good run at the weekend and are ready to get back to the serious bevvying after spending most of Monday detoxing with a few cheap medicinal ones at the 'Start the Week Beer Sale' in The Castle, which the lads on incapacity give a wide berth to, as the bogs are on the first floor since they done it out. The story is the dole have shanghaied the CCTV footage and used it to sanction half the cunts that drink in there. Their line is that if some arsehole with alleged chronic mobility issues can make it up 2 flights of stairs for a slash after a skite of pints before the sun's over the yard arm, then the poor fucker can probably graft for his bit. The big fucking society, eh? Cunts.

So, a pair of breath fresheners later, we tell the Over 60s snakebite connoisseurs and the pulmonary embolism gang who are all smoking tabs in the entrance that we'll see them later and head off down the Job Centre for our weekly Career Crossroads meeting, fighting our way through the front door, past the fleet of bespoke mobility scooters. Some classic designs round here like, based on Lambrettas or Harley Davidsons. Aldo reckons they could shoot a disabled remake of *Quadrophenia* in The Gloucester, with all the Mods having prolapsed discs and the rockers on the sick with emphysema. Honest man, we're still bad laughing at the thought when me and Aldo stop off at Lidl for a few of those 660cl big bottles of German Pils with the twist-off caps, just in case we get delayed. Same time, Stevie calls into Bargain Booze to get his cider prescription filled. Consequently we arrive

to sign on with our customary precision at 11.29 and 45
seconds.

Me and Aldo nearly mess ourselves when the advisor
calls Stevie over to desk 3 and he wanders across doing
that limping sort of dance we learned from that Blazin'
Squad video years back. It's the cue for me and Aldo to
start singing 'meet you at the crossroads, crossroads,
crossroads,' *sotto voce* like, until every other claimant in
the queue joins in, doing the hand signals as well,
because it's sort of our anthem. A kind of 'We Shall
Overcome' for the thirsty, shifty and mad that gets sung
same time, same place every fucking fortnight. I'm
telling you man, there's surreptitiously opened
Perlenbacher leaking out my sneck and Aldo's choking
like some cunt better give him the Heimlich manoeuvre,
while all the dozy fucking dicks who work for the dole
seethe in fake Trappist indignation in their padded office
chairs behind their computer monitors at their veneered
work spaces, because they can't do fuck all about us
cunts. Except maybe sanction Aldo for having a shit
singing voice.

Suddenly, just when you expect the community a
capella to get really fucking loud, the singing stops as
Stevie takes an unrehearsed, slow motion stumble
forward, then plummets towards the broad slice of
horizontal wood that separates the haves and have nots.
It's all going fast again as he smashes his forehead on the
bevelled corner and lands in a messy heap on the
lakeland blue carpet. Nice floor covering that one. You
wouldn't know it was scotchgarded until you see Stevie's
blood running over the lip of the desk and settling in a
pool. None of it's soaking in at all.

Soon as he processes what's going on, Aldo's up out
the chair and in control of the situation, *in loco parentis*.
Starts demanding the security guard gets on the blower to
999, wanting paramedics here immediately to take a look
at her dearest and oldest friend 'ASA fucking P.' I'm

trying to make light of it though, not wanting Stevie to go into shock, saying we'd best get the priest down from St Joseph's as we need to make sure he's got the right support network in place if things go rapidly downhill. Goes down like a lead balloon that one. Half of them look quizzically at me and the rest ignore what I said, so I nip over and try to look after Stevie to stop feeling like a spare prick.

He's fucked like. Awful. Almost as bad as if some fucker had offered him a job, you know. There's a grey tinge to his complexion that's normally a nasty combination of red and yellow, like a Partick Thistle home shirt. Or a Barcelona away one. He's struggling to get up, but eventually he manages to flop over on to all fours, before hoying up the breakfast pints (that bigger puddle didn't soak in the carpet either). Empty, he turns himself round and sits with his back to the desk, blood and sweat sliding down his face.

'Somebody give this poor man a tab,' barks Aldo and this skinny wife whose bad with her nerves and always hides beneath a massive fringe, saying nowt to anyone, sends over a Richmond Superking Menthol that he sparks up without any fucker daring to complain about it.

Stevie is an ugly cunt at the best of times, but today he's extra fucking shan. Matinee idol looks for a video nasty. He's split his eyebrow open, like the time he'd collided with a lamp post coming out of a late one in The Wheatsheaf, but this time it's on his left side. Some young kid from the back office, who is obviously the designated first aider round here, presses a cotton wool pad over the seeping wound, getting Stevie to try and hold it steady while he winds this yellowy, piss coloured crepe bandage several times round Stevie's head, securing it with what appears to be a 70s style nappy pin, giving him the appearance of a homeless participant in a Six Nations scrum, before offering him a glass of water. Fuck that. Stevie, eschewing the restorative qualities of my proffered Rheinheitsgebot influenced carry out, extracts an emergency Strongbow from his inside breast pocket and swallows four codeine one of the back pain squad pass over to him.

Stevie's just putting the tab end out on his shoe when the chief bod in the dole office joins us. Stevie hands him the filter. 'Cheers pal.' The boss is being all pretend sympathetic, but you can tell the cunt wants normality restored, which means getting us out of here double quick. He points out that as First Aid has been administered, there's no obligation for any member of Job Centre Plus staff to call 999 as, in his opinion, paramedics wouldn't do anything different. Aldo's not having that. Explains forcefully that what we've all just witnessed could have had a very negative effect on what is, 'let's face it pal,' a room full of some of the most vulnerable and marginalised members of society. The lost, the lonely and the infirm who in no way can be expected in this instance to go through the fortnightly rigmarole of interrogation and browbeating, before being granted their meagre JSA or other non means tested benefits.

Gesticulating at the assembled flock, Aldo announces with sombre finality, 'These poor cunts are all in shock. Look at them. They need a drink, not the third degree about their noble yet fruitless efforts to secure regular paid employment.'

Meanwhile, I get properly into investigative journalist mode, down on my haunches, searching for evidence as to the cause of Stevie's fall, imperceptibly shifting bits of office furniture, in order to infer their incorrect and indeed hazardous placement has resulted in this unfortunate event that we are all now reaping the bitter harvest of, as well as nimbly loosening the carpet tiles.

I yank at the boss cunt's suit jacket as he looks fearfully down at me, while I solemnly indicate the overlap between a displaced pair of 1 metre Axminister squares, before brandishing the one I have decided to blame for snaring our hero and causing his tumble. 'We need to see the fucking accident book, bonny lad,' Aldo tells the supervisor cunt. 'No doubt it is chocka with evidence of a vainglorious, cavalier attitude to health and safety that will validate our associate's civil claim for damages. Isn't that right comrade?' he inquires of a still visibly shaken Stevie whose need for bevvy now outstrips my requirement for a piss. Either they show me the staff shithouse or I water the assembled collection of tax payers' yucca plants with a quart of metabolised Stella.

Before I have time to vocalise my requirements, boss twat bows to the inevitable and announces that all appointments were now cancelled and payments would be processed in due course, on account of a medical emergency. When Mr Suit suggests we take Stevie up to the walk-in centre, Aldo snorts with derision, saying Stevie was in no fit state to walk anywhere and consequently extracts a brand new twenty from the supervisor's wallet to defray our necessary taxi expenses. It's our cue to go. Like those far off days when the head teacher used to get you in the hall at Juniors and say school was cancelled as the heating was fucked or the caretakers were going on strike, news of our afternoon's freedom causes a ripple of joy that soon spreads to a tumult of ecstasy as 50 freed long term claimants pour on to the High Street, wondering whether The Metropole, The Half Moon or Curley's would get their trade. 'Good decision my man,' announces Aldo, 'but you can expect to be hearing from our solicitors in due course.'

It's straight back up the hill to The Gloucester where Dr Aldo diagnoses Stevie as suffering from acute sobriety syndrome and prescribes a large brandy on the house, wangled out of Janice the barmaid by a complex, embellished retelling of the events of the morning, so as to make Stevie's continued existence the kind of miracle not seen outside the Old Testament.

I'm half wondering whether we should actually take Stevie down the walk-in centre to get his head properly looked at, especially as when he passed out in The Star about six months back, they sent him up the General for some tests. Gave him a brain scan and that. The docs told him he needed to stop drinking immediately until they found out exactly what caused it. He didn't like that. Just never went back for the results. Well, the appointment they gave him was for a Friday afternoon, you know. No news is bad news I suppose. Of course in the end, we don't go anywhere and it ends up being a normal Tuesday.

Several pints and a series of rapid interchanges between the Racing Channel and Hits TV allows the majority of the gathered clientele to engage in their pecuniary interest in the sport of kings, while our choreographic obsession with Blazin' Squad is taken to new heights as, after the last race at Haydock Park, the whole fucking room erupts when 'Crossroads' comes on at number 13 in 100 Best Boyband Hits. Me, Stevie and Aldo word perfect on it, escorting Janice, out on an empties mission, across the bar in a full-on rendition of the song and the dance. Then we raise a glass to Kenzie, Reeper, Flava and the rest of the daft fuckers, before turning the telly over to Kerrang, which was showing 'The Dead Flag Blues' by Godspeed You! Black Emperor. Aldo keeps hold of the remote and jams the volume up full, shouting above the noise that 'this is what I fucking call dance music,' which clears the afternoon punters from the bar. It's like a disabled Brands Hatch, seeing all the mobility scooters jockeying for position at the corner.

Then, it's just the three of us pondering what exactly GY!BE meant by the line 'we're trapped in the belly of this horrible machine and the machine is bleeding to death' over a last pint, before Aldo calls a taxi as his lass wants him home for his tea. So we drink up. Canny day out I suppose.

JOE ENGLAND
Drinking In The Daylight

One of the few pleasures life still offers me is the dignity of my lunchtime pint. I lost my wife Elspeth fifteen years ago next month. We used to drink in the pub and club at weekends. This side of London has always been a tough place to live, but I have nothing but very fond memories of growing up around here. When the war was over there was so much fun to be had on bombsites. I came from a poor family but we didn't know any better. I enjoyed my childhood. It was special. Wouldn't ever change a thing. We made our own fun. Looked out for each other. Not like these days. Times have changed.

I met Elspeth at school. We were married at seventeen. We never had children. But that's another story. Everyone used to say we were the epitome of a happy marriage. I think we were envied by many. A few no doubt would have loved to have seen us fall out. Make them feel better about their own weaknesses in love. But that was never going to happen to us. Believe me, I never once raised my voice to her.

Anyway, yes, we used to always go out in an evening come the weekend. From Thursday to Sunday. I haven't been out in an evening since...well, when exactly that last time was, I simply couldn't tell you.

This side of London has always been a tough place to live and at night these days it's the kind of place the likes of me should never be out in.

I, all of us know, about not making ourselves vulnerable. It's called being street wise. Lots of idiots round these parts like a bit of old man bashing. I know a few sickening stories. We all do. That's why you'll always find the pubs filled with our age group come lunchtime. Drinking in the daylight we call it. The hospital drinking lounge the cynics call us. One last drink or two from the grave. But forget them. I am not scared of death or anyone. But I am not the man I once was. I am very thoughtful. I think a great deal, about things. About the past, my life, my Elspeth, and so many good friends gone.

Today when I got to the pub for my lunchtime pint, I saw that the front windows were boarded up, but the door was open.

Inside, I noticed how the pool table had the wooden cover on, which was as much as a surprise to me as the boarded up windows. There also didn't appear to be many chairs. A few familiar faces stood head-bowed at the bar, hardly glancing up to notice my arrival.

I ordered a pint of Carlsberg Cold in a straight glass. Ernie the landlord was serving. He didn't say, 'Morning Bill' or smile. He just poured my pint. I wanted to ask him what had happened. But I then appreciated that he was sweating, eyes fat and watery, face red with stress.

So I bought my pint, thanked him and sat in the corner at the rear of the pub where some chairs were and by the only window left and letting in the light.

I hadn't even begun to read my paper when I was joined by one-eyed Albert; even by sitting in the light I never saw him coming towards me from the bar. He had a serious look of concern on his face and had brought his pint along with him, so I folded my paper and watched him as he sat down opposite and supped on his pale ale and lager.

'Want to know about what happened last night in here then?' he said, lifting the patch from his left eye and scratching the unseen glass and skin beneath. It was clear to me that Albert wasn't going away and there was no point in being rude as we'd known each other a lifetime, so I nodded. He continued: 'Two brick-shithouses in suits accompanied by a Brief came in here straight from court. Do you know who they were? I'll tell you. Only Billy Greenaway and Dennis Morris. They got away with it. Can you believe that? You never heard silence like it when the door opened. Pair of them stood there. Jolly Green Giants. They then remained rooted at the bar all night long – like robots, never even going for a piss – and got hammered while their Brief sat perched from your position there. On the one occasion he moved from that seat to the bar to deliver gentle words of legal guidance, he was colourfully told about his current rightful place and took the words wisely and fled. The next thing to happen was the two Dan's getting thrown through glass and all hell broke loose. Billy Greenaway and Dennis Morris eventually lost the war. But they put up a fight. That was never in question. But two versus forty odd – regardless of who started it – is not fair play. I heard, we all reckon, there will be a serious reprisal coming. Ernie is a worried man. We're all worried men. That this place is gonna get petrol-bombed. You know only too well how dirty they play, the form of them two. Not good times to be drinking in here, eh.'

When Albert slouched off back to the bar, I went outside with my paper, leaving nearly a full pint. Minding who was about when I came out the pub, I then went down the Working Men's; at least this was an establishment that looked after its customers, kept out the riff-raff, because they definitely did that, where an old man could enjoy the solitude of his paper and lunchtime pint in peace.

FORD DAGENHAM
Laugh Our Death Away

the
moon is a blur
a smudge
a moody streetlight
a stain
in the frozen fog dawn
all
complex simple
like
jazz

i'm alive i'm alive
out
in
nature

but
i
head to work
head to manmade walls
head to
windlowless shoebox architecture
where
we'll
hope out loud in the day dungeon
laughing
our
death away

WORDS ABOUT THE CONTRIBUTORS

P.A. Levy was born and bred in East London and he is the founding member of the Clueless Collective. He supports West Ham United.

Michael Keenaghan is a prolific London writer and his crime fiction has featured in all issues of PUSH.

Joseph Ridgwell is from East London. He is the author of many small press books and also, my indispensable right-hand man.

Dickson Telfer lives in Falkirk and supports East Stirlingshire. His short fiction collections, *The Red Man Turns to Green* and *Refrigerator Cake*, are published by Fledgling Press.

Tim Wells is made of reggae, pie and mash, lager top and Leyton Orient FC.

Simon Dent was born in Hillingdon and now lives in Catford. Suffering Fulham FC regular.

Jamie Hall is the youngest contributor to date to be published in PUSH. West Ham United season ticket holder who goes to as many away games as home.

Ian Cusack watches a lot of grass roots football; also the editor of the Newcastle United fanzine, *The Popular Side*.

J. A. Carnie is from Essex. *Three Goals Last Season* and *Takeaway* were both published in issue 11.

Anneliese McMillan Gregg is from Derry and her poem *Young* was also published in issue 11.

Steve Finbow lives in Walthamstow and he is currently working on *Notes from the Sick Room*, a book about illness and creativity.

John King is the author of seven novels. He lives in London. Supports Chelsea FC.

Ford Dagenham is a poet and the author of *Canvey Island of the Mind* published by Blackheath Books. He lives in South Essex.

Jim Gibson lives in Nottingham and runs the anarchic literary zine, *Hand Job*.

Jon Tait is the 'Barearse Boy' from Northumberland who now lives in Carlisle.

Kevin Williamson is the founder of Rebel Inc. In 2011 he launched Neu! Reekie! with Michael Pedersen. Easter Road regular.

Wayne Holloway is a writer/director based in London. His first book *Land of Hunger* is to be published this year.

Paul Reaney has never played for Leeds United. A writer and librarian well into his music.

Dean Lilleyman is the author of the brutal but excellent debut, *Billy and the Devil*. Currently working on a second novel.

Martin Hayes is an Irish writer and author of the graphic novels, *Project Luna: 1947* and *Aleister Crowley: Wandering the Waste*. He lives in County Wicklow.

Anette Roller lives in Munich and she has had poetry and fiction published in four issues.

Jenni Doherty is a poet and author of *Rain Spill* published by Guildhall Press. Jenni also runs the excellent Little Acorns Bookstore in Derry.

Raymond Gorman is the former songwriter/guitarist of That Petrol Emotion. His new band, The Everlasting Yeah, have a debut album, *Anima Rising*, out now.

Andrew Taylor is a Liverpool poet who supports Everton. He co-edits *erbacce*.

Craig Gibson is the editor of Edinburgh's finest publication, *One O'Clock Gun*.

Thomas McColl lives in Stratford, East London. *Chip Shop Aquarians* first appeared in issue 16.

Gary Budden is the co-editor of London based, Influx Press.

ACKNOWLEDGEMENTS

To Dickson Telfer, a talented writer and performer, who once again undertook at short notice, a thorough proof read. An absolute diamond.

To Paul Talling for kindly allowing me to continue to use his Derelict London photography on so many of the covers.

To Jose Arroyo for his original woodcut artwork, and as I have said to the world so many times, you are a genius mate.

To John King for his support and friendship.

To Kosmo Vinyl and Graham Want for their superb work with the jacket design.

To Jim Dalton who prints each issue of PUSH. You may support Charlton Athletic, but you are a true gentleman.

To East London Press for their continued faith.

Thank You to all the contributors, not only those featured in this book, but everyone who has to date appeared in PUSH.

And just as important, to all those who have bought and still continue to buy a copy.

Love you all.

EAST LONDON PRESS

PUSH – BEST OF THE FIRST 10 ISSUES

JAH WOBBLE, DAVID PEACE

East London Press was founded in 2014. We publish writers and artists whose work reflects subculture and the local communities in which they inhabit. We believe a good book can change the world. The first book to be published by East London Press was our first anthology of Joe England's PUSH magazine.

'If someone asked me where a future Gerard Kersh, Alan Sillitoe or Irvine Welsh might be found, I would tell them to buy a copy of PUSH' – John King

'PUSH is great, excellent reading' – Irvine Welsh

£7.99

eastlondonpress.bigcartel.com

EAST LONDON PRESS

THE GIRL WHO ATE NEW YORK

H.P. TINKER

We are proud to announce our second publication. 15 comically surreal love stories from the influential and highly original short fiction writer, H.P. Tinker.

'Unsung comic genius'
– Time Out

'Hilarious deadpan surrealism'
– The Times

'Tinker is Barthelme and Pynchon in their prime'
– The Guardian

£9.99

eastlondonpress.bigcartel.com